General Science:
Introductory Facts and Concepts
Volume One

by

Katherine Davey

Julie Pigott

Irwin Worshell

Legal deposit – Bibliothèque et Archives nationales du Québec, 2011
Legal deposit – Library and Archives Canada, 2011

ISBN 978-2-923623-72-6

Printed in Canada

Catalog Number: TBCE3-1

Reviewers:
Steve Brayne
Denis Lapierre

Editor-In-Chief:
Ernest Smith, Ph.D.

Copy Editor:
Joanne Labre

Design and Cover:
Geneviève Ouimet

Table of Contents

Table of Contents

Table of Contents

Table of Contents

ECOLOGY UNIT 1

Introduction to Ecosystems

Lesson #1 – The Ecosystem Concept

> **Objectives:**
>
> • Define ecological community
>
> • Define the concept of an ecosystem
>
> • List and describe the living and non-living parts of an ecosystem

Introduction

If you have ever taken a moment to observe the different plants and animals in a park or a forest, you probably noticed a variety of interactions. A bee pollinates a flower. A deer eats a tree shoot. A bird builds its nest on a tree branch. An earthworm lives in the soil.

These interactions are part of the study of ecology. Ecology is the study of the interactions between living things and their environment. Plants and animals depend on the environment and each other to meet their basic needs for food, water, and shelter. This dependence creates a variety of interactions that you will be studying in this unit.

You also may have noticed that the park or forest has been affected by human activity. A tree has been cut down. A path winds through the forest. Flowers are planted in a garden. Some litter is left behind in the park.

Humans, too, are part of the interactions between living things and their environment. We depend on nature to supply us with different resources to meet our needs for food, water and shelter. For this reason it is important that we learn how nature works. In this unit, you will also learn about the different processes that occur in nature and how human activity affects these processes.

Communities and Ecosystems

An organism, or any living thing, does not exist independently in nature. When we study ecology, we are interested in the many ways that an organism is linked to other living things and to its environment. For instance, a mouse in the forest depends on plants for its food, a hollowed out tree for its shelter, and the sun for warmth. Its fur may be a home for insects. The mouse competes with other mice for its food and shelter. Snakes and owls may depend on the mouse for food. Other organisms may feed on the mouse's waste. These are only some of the possible interactions between the mouse, other organisms, and its environment. In fact, there are many connections that link any organism, groups of organisms, and the environment.

Let's first consider the connections between organisms. Organisms of the same kind, or species, often occur in the same area. We use the term population to describe a group of organisms of the same species that occupy a certain area. The mice in the forest, the trout in a lake, or the people in the country are different examples of populations. The place where a population lives is also called a habitat. The habitat can be a large forest or a hollowed out log. Many different populations can be found in a single habitat.

The populations in a habitat interact with each other. As described earlier, the mouse population interacts with the snake population, the tree population, and the insect population. These populations interact with each other to meet their special needs for food and shelter. A community is a group of interacting populations living in a particular place. Just as you live in a community of different kinds of people who interact with each other, livings things in the natural world also exist in communities. In the previous example, all of the mice, plants, trees, insects, snakes, and owls in that particular forest form a community.

It would be difficult to study a community without considering the influence of the environmental factors such as the sun, rain, and soil. A spring with little rain could kill some of the plants that the mice depend on for food. If the numbers of mice decreased the other species in the community would also be affected. Since the environment plays such an important role in the survival of living things, ecologists study communities together with their environment. An ecosystem is a community of living things together with its environment. When you study an ecosystem you consider all of interactions that occur between organisms and their environments. For example all of the plants, animals and microorganisms living in a forest, together with the air, soil, nutrients, water, wind, and sun make up a forest ecosystem.

Ecosystems can be very small or very large, depending on the area you choose to study. An aquatic ecosystem can be as small as a puddle or as large as the

Pacific Ocean. A meadow, a forest, or a mountain range are examples of different kinds and sizes of terrestrial ecosystems. Each of these ecosystems are made up of different communities and are influenced by different environmental factors. If you put together all of Earth's ecosystems, you would have the biosphere, the regions on Earth where life exists.

Components of an Ecosystem

An ecosystem is made up of living and nonliving things. The living things in an ecosystem are referred to as the biotic factors whereas the nonliving things are the abiotic factors. The abiotic factors include the sun, air, soil, water, and nutrients. Anything that you might

Ecosystem

organism

population

community

ecosystem

biosphere

consider as the environment can usually be categorized as an abiotic factor. The abiotic factors are important because they influence what kind of life can exist within a particular area. For instance, you wouldn't expect to find the same fish or plants in a lake as in the ocean. Fish that survive well in the ocean's saltwater are not well suited to the fresh water of a lake. Similarly, you would see different trees in a forest in Eastern Canada than in a forest in South America. The nutrients, sunlight, rainfall in each forest play a role in determining what kinds of trees can grow. The many different abiotic factors limit the types of plants and animals that can survive in an ecosystem.

The biotic factors are any plant, animal, or microorganism that live in the ecosystem. There are potentially thousands of different living things in any given ecosystem. However, the biotic factors in an ecosystem can be classified into two main groups, producers and consumers. Producers, or autotrophs ("auto" means own, and "troph" means food), are so named because they produce their own food. Most producers are green plants. Green plants make their own food by capturing the energy from the sun and converting it to sugar by a process called photosynthesis.

Word Equation for Photosynthesis

$$6\ CO_2 + 6\ H_2O \xrightarrow{\text{+ sunlight (solar energy)}} C_6H_{12}O_6 + 6\ O_2$$

carbon dioxide   water   carbohydrate   oxygen

All other organisms are consumers or heterotrophs ("hetero" means other). Consumers must eat other organisms to obtain energy. Based on what they eat, consumers can be classified into several different categories:

• Herbivores are the vegetarians of the natural world; these animals eat plants only. Rabbits, elephants, caterpillars and whales are examples of herbivores.

• Carnivores are meat eaters and feed exclusively on other animals. Eagles, lions, and some species of sharks are carnivores.

• Omnivores have a diet of both plants and animals. Some examples of omnivores are bears, foxes and pigs.

• Scavengers feed on larger dead organisms. When you see flies on a dead animal, this is an example of a scavenger getting its food. Hyenas and vultures are other examples of scavengers.

• Detritivores feed on smaller dead organisms and waste. Earthworms, crabs and beetles are detritivores.

• Decomposers are a type of detritivore that break down any remaining dead organisms or waste, releasing nutrients back into the ecosystem. These recyclers of the ecosystem include bacteria and fungi.

Lesson Summary

1. Organisms are linked to other living things and to their environment.

2. A population is a group of organisms of the same species that occupy a certain area. The place where a population lives is also called a habitat.

3. A community is a group of interacting populations living in the same habitat.

4. An ecosystem is a community of living things together with its environment. These ecosystems can be very small or very large.

5. Living parts of an ecosystem are referred to as biotic. Non-living parts are referred to as abiotic. The biotic factors are either producers or consumers.

Lesson #1 – Questions

1. What is the difference between a community and a population?

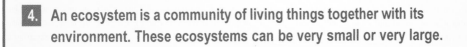

_____

_____

_____

_____

2. Define the concept of an ecosystem.

_____

_____

_____

_____

Lesson #1 – Questions (continued)

3. Give one example of a biotic factor and one example of an abiotic factor in an ecosystem.

_____

_____

_____

_____

_____

_____

_____

4. Explain why green plants are called producers.

_____

_____

_____

_____

_____

_____

_____

5. Name the type of organism (herbivore, omnivore, etc) that each of these definitions describe:

(a) Organisms that must eat other organisms to survive _____

(b) Animals that eat both plants and animals _____

(c) Organisms that break down dead organism and waste, releasing nutrients to the ecosystem _____

(d) Animals that eat plants only _____

Lesson #2 – Energy Flow in an Ecosystem

Objectives:

- Analyze a food chain by placing organisms in trophic levels

- Summarize how energy flows through an ecosystem

- Explain why some organisms outnumber others in an ecosystem

Food Chains

All organisms in an ecosystem need energy to survive. This energy is obtained through food. As you learned in the first lesson, producers obtain energy by making their own food whereas consumers must feed on other organisms for energy. This dependence on other organisms for food leads to feeding relationships that interconnect all living things in an ecosystem. A food chain illustrates the simplest kind of feeding relationship. For example, in a forest ecosystem, a grasshopper feeds on plants. The grasshopper is consumed by a spider and the spider is eaten by a bird. Finally, that bird is hunted by a hawk. A food chain clearly shows this pathway of food consumption.

You could probably think of another food chain for a forest ecosystem. In fact, many different food chains exist in ecosystems. Although there are many different kinds of food chains, each food chain follows the same general pattern. A link in a food chain is called a trophic, or feeding level. The trophic levels are numbered as the first, second, third, and fourth levels, starting with the producers.

Illustration of Food Chain

| plant | grasshopper | spider | bird | hawk |

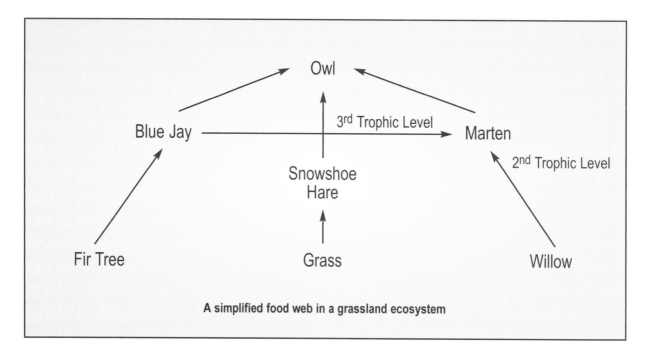

A simplified food web in a grassland ecosystem

Each of the trophic levels is occupied by a certain kind of organism. Producers are always in the first trophic level since they do not feed on another organism. Consumers occupy the rest of the trophic levels. The second trophic level is the first consumer in the food chain and is called a primary consumer. Primary consumers eat plants and are therefore herbivores or omnivores. The next consumer in the food chain is the secondary consumer. The secondary consumer is in the third trophic level. Since the secondary consumer feeds on another animal, it is a carnivore or an omnivore. Similarly, the tertiary consumer occupies the fourth trophic level, and is a carnivore. The last link in a food chain is also referred to as the top carnivore since it is at the top of the food chain and is not hunted by other animals.

Food Webs

A food chain is a simplified version of what really happens in an ecosystem. An organism will feed on more than one plant or animal and will be eaten by more than one animal. In this way many links are formed between organisms and some animals may occupy more than one trophic level. These complex feeding relationships form a food web. A food web shows the interconnected feeding relationships in an ecosystem. A simplified food web in a grassland ecosystem is shown above. In this food web, the marten could be considered both as a primary consumer and as a secondary consumer. When it feeds on willows, it is in the second trophic level, but when it feeds on blue jays, it is in the third trophic level. In reality, the food web would contain many more participants and therefore many more interrelationships.

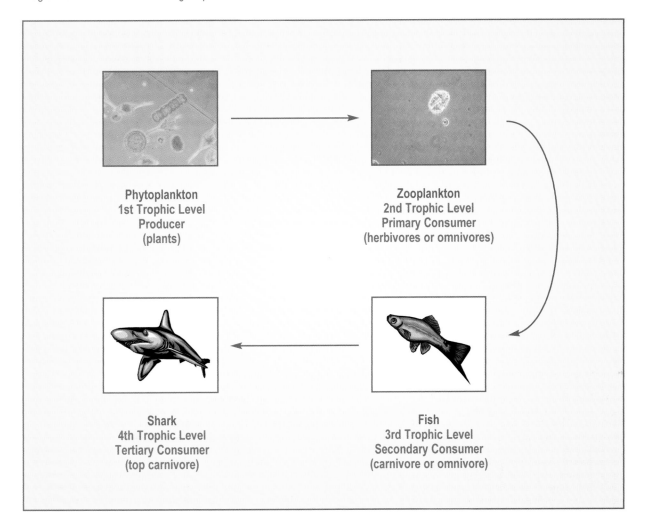

Detritus feeders and Decomposers

An essential feeding relationship not included in most food chains are formed by detritus feeders and decomposers. These feed on the waste and dead organisms at every trophic level. For example, the earthworm is a common detritus feeder. It feeds on dead leaves, excreting waste. Decomposers such as fungi and bacteria will use the earthworm's waste as a source of organisms energy, extracting the nutrients they need and releasing any leftover nutrients into the ecosystem.

The presence of decomposers and detritus feeders means that dead organisms and waste are always broken down and hardly any matter is wasted. Since the remaining nutrients are made available to the ecosystem, the soil, water and atmosphere are replenished with essential molecules. Without the detritus feeders and decomposers, the supply of nutrients would be exhausted and life could not be sustained in the ecosystem. This important process will be discussed further in an upcoming lesson.

Energy Flow

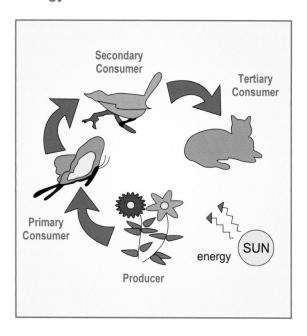

Diagram of Energy Flow

When a snake consumes a mouse, the snake is gaining energy from the mouse. This transfer of energy is one of the most important processes in all ecosystems. A food chain not only shows feeding relationships between organisms, it also shows how energy flows through an ecosystem. Energy flow starts with the sun, which is the source of energy for ecosystems. The sun's energy is captured by the green plants or the producers.

Producers are vital to ecosystems as they bring the sun's energy into the ecosystem, making it available to other organisms. As you learned earlier, a green plant captures solar energy to make sugar through photosynthesis. The plant uses this sugar for energy. Then, the energy stored by the plant is passed on to whichever organism consumes it. As one organism consumes another, energy flows from one trophic level to the next trophic level of the food chain. The energy flow in a food chain is always in one direction, starting with the producer, and finishing with the last trophic level.

The energy transfer from trophic level to trophic level is inefficient. Energy is lost at each step of the food chain. Once a plant captures the sun's energy, most of the energy is used up by the plant to live and grow, some of it is wasted (through heat) and a very small amount of it is stored. When the plant is eaten by a caterpillar, only the plant's stored energy is available to the caterpillar. Similarly the caterpillar will use most of the energy it acquired to live and grow. Some

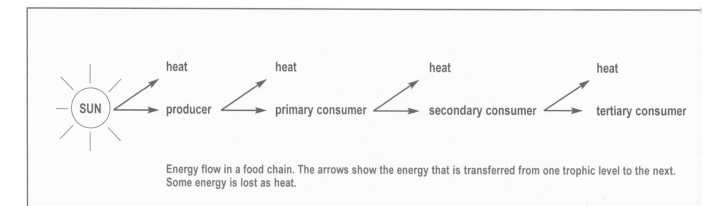

Energy flow in a food chain. The arrows show the energy that is transferred from one trophic level to the next. Some energy is lost as heat.

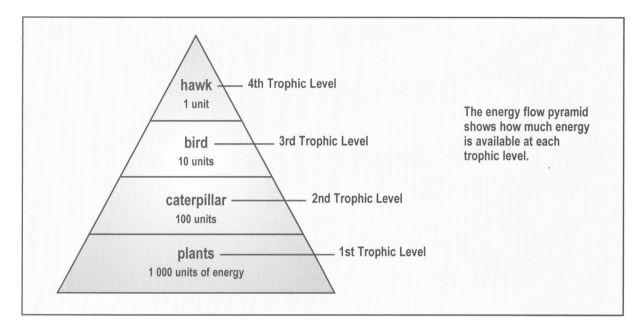

The energy flow pyramid shows how much energy is available at each trophic level.

of the energy is wasted and a relatively small amount is stored. The caterpillar's stored energy is available to the next consumer in the chain. On average, only 10% of the energy captured by an organism is passed on to the next trophic level. If a plant captures 1000 units of energy from the sun, only 100 units will be available to the caterpillar. When a bird consumes the caterpillar, only 10 units of the original 1000 that entered the food chain are available for the bird.

An energy flow pyramid illustrates this pattern of energy flow. Notice how the producers have the most energy available to them. As you can see, as we move up trophic levels there is less and less energy available to the organisms. This explains why food chains rarely have more than 4 or 5 trophic levels. Otherwise, too much energy is lost and there is not enough energy to support the organisms in the higher trophic levels.

Trophic Level Consumers

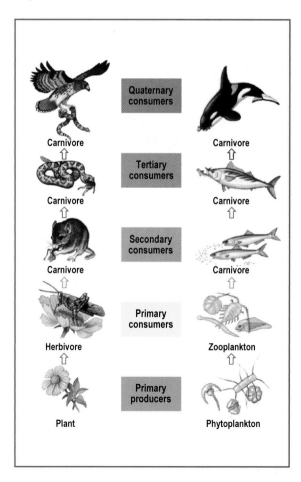

Pyramid of Numbers

Diagram of Pyramid of Numbers

It might be easier for you to consider this energy flow pyramid in terms of numbers of organisms. If you take a hike through a forest, you will immediately notice that the green plants outnumber any of the other organisms. Producers are most numerous in an ecosystem because there is a lot of energy available to support them. You might see a number of primary consumers such as grasshoppers, deer, caterpillars, or mice, but there are fewer of these organisms than the green plants. Finally, if you are lucky, you might see a single top carnivore such as a hawk or a wolf. Since there is relatively little energy available to these top carnivores, there are very few of them. This pattern is illustrated by a pyramid of numbers.

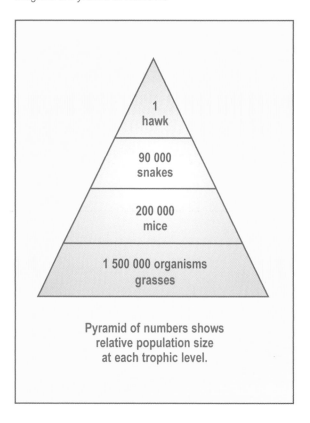

Pyramid of numbers shows relative population size at each trophic level.

Lesson Summary

1. Living organisms obtain energy through food. A food chain describes a simple feeding relationship among living things.

2. A food web shows the interconnected feeding relationships in an ecosystem.

3. Detritus feeders and decomposers feed on dead organisms and waste materials.

4. Energy is lost at each step in the food chain.

Lesson #2 – Questions

1. According to the following food chain

Grass $\longrightarrow$ prairie dog $\longrightarrow$ coyote $\longrightarrow$ golden eagle

(a) Which organism is the producer?

_____
_____
_____

(b) Which organism occupies the second trophic level?

_____
_____
_____

(c) Which organism is the tertiary consumer?

_____
_____
_____

(d) Which organism has the most energy available?

_____
_____
_____

(e) Which organism is most likely to have the smallest population in the ecosystem?

_____
_____
_____ $\Rightarrow$

Lesson #2 – Questions (continued)

2. What is the role of detritus feeders and decomposers in a food chain?

_____

_____

_____

_____

_____

_____

_____

_____

3. Explain how energy is transferred from the sun to the last, or highest, trophic level of a food chain.

_____

_____

_____

_____

_____

_____

_____

_____

_____

4. Why are there seldom more than four links in a food chain?

_____

_____

_____

_____

_____

_____

_____

_____

Life Cycles

Lesson #3 – Nutrient Cycles

Objectives:

• Name two examples of nutrients

• Define the concept of a nutrient cycle

• Explain why nutrients are cycled through an ecosystem

Nutrient Cycles

As you learned in the previous lesson, all organisms need energy to survive. This energy is continually supplied to ecosystems by the sun. The energy flows one way through food chains, starting with the producers. In addition to energy, organisms need certain building materials, or chemical elements to survive. The elements oxygen, nitrogen, and carbon are only a few of these building materials. Unlike energy, these chemical elements are not continually supplied to ecosystems. These elements are in limited supply in the air, soil and water. So, in order to keep ecosystems supplied with all of the building materials for life, these elements are recycled and reused over and over again. For instance, as you are breathing, you are taking in oxygen from the atmosphere. There are billions of other people on the Earth who are using the oxygen in the atmosphere, but the oxygen does not run out. The oxygen you are breathing in will eventually be returned to the environment and used by another organism. Also, the oxygen you are breathing in has been used by other organisms before it was returned to the atmosphere for you to use. Just think, the oxygen that is filling your lungs now may have been inhaled by your grandmother or even George Washington. You will be learning how these chemical elements, also known as nutrients, are recycled and reused in ecosystems.

Nutrients are the chemical elements, or building materials, organisms need to survive. Some nutrients such as carbon, oxygen, nitrogen, hydrogen, phosphorus and sulphur are needed in large quantities. Nutrients such as sodium, zinc, copper and iodine are needed in very small amounts. Found in the air, soil, or water, nutrients are taken up by organisms and put to use for growth, maintenance, and repair. Eventually, the nutrients return to the physical environment to be used by another organism. A nutrient cycle is the movement of the nutrients through the ecosystem, from the physical environment to organisms and back to the environment again. This constant recycling of nutrients is an important process in ecosystems. Without these life cycles, the nutrients would be depleted and the organisms in the ecosystem would die. Imagine what would happen if oxygen did not get recycled and there wasn't enough oxygen for us to breathe. In the next lessons you will study how carbon, nitrogen, phosphorus and water are recycled and reused in ecosystems.

Lesson Summary

1. Energy is supplied to ecosystems by the sun.

2. Nutrients are the building materials that organisms need to survive.

3. The constant recycling of nutrients is an important process in ecosystems.

Lesson #3 – Questions

1. What is a nutrient cycle?

_____

_____

_____

_____

_____

_____

_____

2. Name two nutrients that cycle in ecosystems.

_____

_____

_____

_____

_____

_____

_____

_____

_____

3. What would happen if nutrients did not cycle in an ecosystem?

_____

_____

_____

_____

_____

_____

_____

_____

_____

_____

Lesson #4 – The Carbon Cycle

Carbon Cycle

A tiny seed germinates in a field and, over the years, grows into a towering tree. A tiny seed can become a giant tree by taking in carbon through the process of photosynthesis. Remember that photosynthesis is the process by which green plants make their own food.

$$6\ CO_2 + 6\ H_2O \longrightarrow C_6H_{12}O_6 + 6\ O_2$$

The tree takes carbon from the air, in the form of carbon dioxide, and with the energy of the sun turns it into carbohydrates. Some of the carbohydrates are then broken down by the tree, freeing the carbon for use as a building block for proteins, fats, and nucleic acids. In this way the tree makes its own food and then builds tissues, growing larger and larger.

The tree, as do all other living things, needs a supply of carbon for survival. Carbon is essential to all life. It is the building block of all organic molecules such as carbohydrates, proteins, fats, and nucleic acids. In terrestrial ecosystems, green plants get their carbon from the atmosphere in the form of carbon dioxide. Carbon dioxide makes up 0.03% of the atmosphere. In aquatic ecosystems, the green plants and photosynthetic bacteria get their carbon from the carbon dioxide that is dissolved in the water. The lakes and oceans hold more than 50 times as much carbon as the atmosphere. All animals get their carbon by consuming other organisms.

The atmosphere and the oceans are reservoirs of carbon in ecosystems. The green plants remove the carbon from the atmosphere or the oceans in the form of carbon dioxide, and through the process of photosynthesis, incorporate the carbon in their tissues. As all of the green plants in the many different ecosystems on Earth repeat this process, more and more carbon dioxide is removed from the carbon reservoirs. Since there is not an endless supply of carbon dioxide in the air and oceans, this supply needs to be replenished. Carbon dioxide will eventually return to the atmosphere and the oceans through the carbon cycle.

Photosynthesis is an important part of the carbon cycle. Once the tree has taken up the carbon found in the air and incorporated it into carbohydrates, the carbon is available to the organisms that consume the tree. When a leaf from the tree is eaten by a deer, the deer breaks down the carbon compounds in the leaf and uses the carbon for building its own tissues. If a wolf preys upon the deer, the wolf uses the carbon in the deer's molecules to build its carbohydrates, proteins or fats. In this way, the carbon that once was part of a carbon dioxide molecule in the air is now incorporated into the molecules of the wolf. Photosynthesis is important to the carbon cycle because it moves the carbon from the atmosphere into the food chain. Then, the carbon moves through the food chain as one organism is eaten by another.

Now that the carbon has entered and moved through the food chain, it must somehow be returned to the atmosphere or oceans. This is accomplished through the process of cellular respiration. Cellular respiration is the process by which all organisms break down carbohydrates for energy.

Your own body is carrying out this process right now. The oxygen that you breathe in is used to help break down carbohydrates, releasing energy to be used by your body. Notice that one of the other products of cellular respiration is carbon dioxide. You do not need carbon dioxide, so your body releases it when you breathe out. Similarly, as the tree, deer, or wolf break down carbohydrates for energy, carbon dioxide is released as waste and returns to the atmosphere. The carbon that was used by the tree to grow moved through the food chain and was released back to the atmosphere. The carbon is now available for another plant.

When an organism dies, it still contains carbon. This carbon is returned to the atmosphere through the work of decomposers. As the decomposers feed on the dead organic matter, they break down the carbohydrates they ingest through the process of cellular respiration. As a result, even more carbon dioxide is returned to the atmosphere In this way there is very little waste in the ecosystems. Any dead organic matter, whether it be waste or dead organisms, is used by the decomposers as food, releasing the carbon to the atmosphere for use by other plants.

The diagram on the next page summarizes the carbon cycle. Note how the carbon cycles from the abiotic part of the ecosystem, the atmosphere, to the biotic part of the ecosystems, the food chain, and back again to the atmosphere.

$$6\ O_2 + C_6H_{12}O_6 \longrightarrow 6\ CO_2 + 6\ H_2O + ENERGY$$

oxygen carbohydrate   carbon   water
                         dioxide

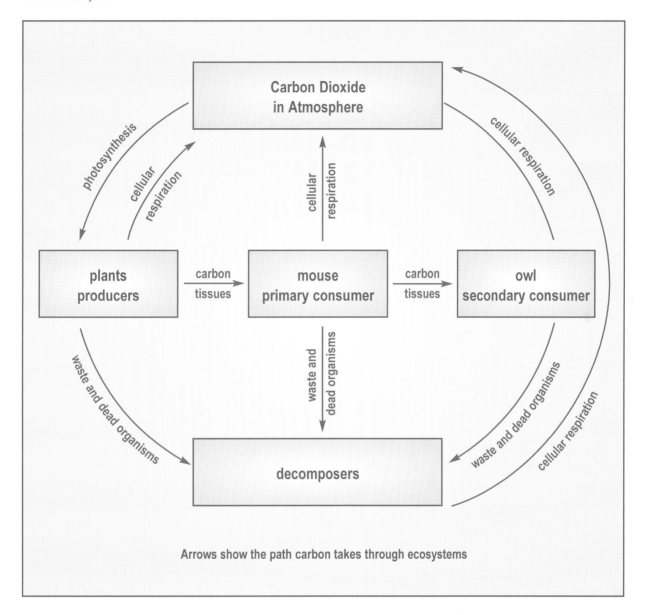

Arrows show the path carbon takes through ecosystems

Aquatic Ecosystems

Carbon is also cycled in aquatic ecosystems. Oceans and lakes contain most of the world's carbon. Carbon dioxide from the air readily dissolves in the oceans or lakes. The various water plants use the dissolved carbon dioxide for photosynthesis and the carbon cycle continues as it does on land. There is one difference, however.

Many sea animals use the carbon they acquire to build their shells. These sea animals include snails, coral, oysters, and barnacles. When these animals die, the shells do not decompose. The shells, with the carbon trapped inside, sink to the bottom of the ocean, eventually becoming part of the bedrock on the ocean floor. When the carbon is locked into the bedrock, it is no longer available to any parts of the food chain. In this way carbon is removed from the carbon cycle. The carbon may re-enter the cycle millions of years later if the rock is pushed to the surface. Rain and wind slowly weathers the rock, releasing the carbon.

Human Activities and the Carbon Cycle

By comparing the chemical equations for photosynthesis and cellular respiration, you will see how these two processes form a cycle. Photosynthesis uses carbon dioxide from the atmosphere, and produces oxygen. Cellular respiration uses oxygen and returns the carbon dioxide to the atmosphere. Through the processes of photosynthesis and cellular respiration, carbon moves from the environment into living tissues and back to the environment again. These processes are balanced to maintain the level of carbon dioxide in the atmosphere. The amount of carbon dioxide used for photosynthesis tends to equal the amount of carbon dioxide released by cellular respiration.

The Carbon Cycle in Aquatic Ecosystem

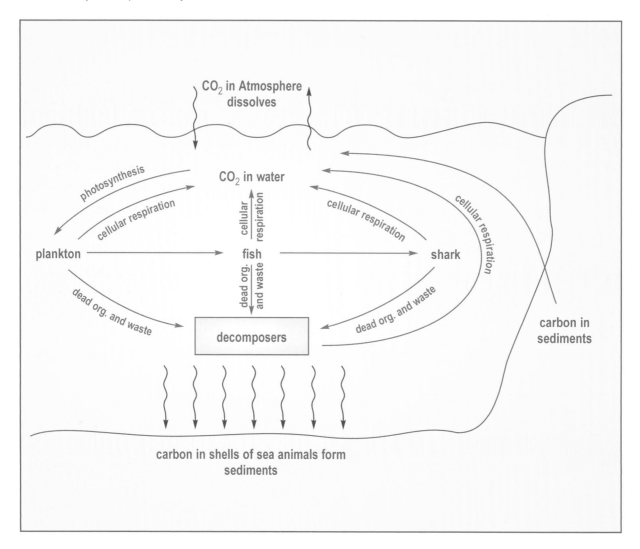

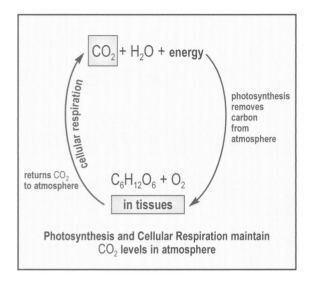

CO_2 + H_2O + energy

cellular respiration

photosynthesis removes carbon from atmosphere

returns CO_2 to atmosphere

$C_6H_{12}O_6$ + O_2

in tissues

Photosynthesis and Cellular Respiration maintain CO_2 levels in atmosphere

Human activities have disrupted the balance of the carbon cycle. You have probably heard reports of global warming. Global warming is largely due to the fact that there is too much carbon dioxide in the atmosphere. The carbon dioxide acts as a blanket, keeping the Earth warm. The warming caused by the carbon dioxide blanket is also called the **greenhouse effect**. Too much carbon dioxide makes a thicker blanket and

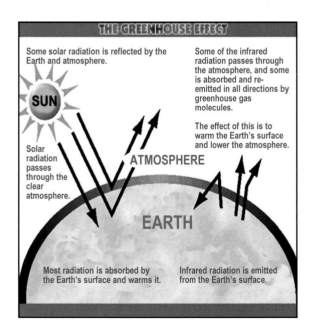

THE GREENHOUSE EFFECT

Some solar radiation is reflected by the Earth and atmosphere.

Some of the infrared radiation passes through the atmosphere, and some is absorbed and re-emitted in all directions by greenhouse gas molecules.

The effect of this is to warm the Earth's surface and lower the atmosphere.

SUN

Solar radiation passes through the clear atmosphere.

ATMOSPHERE

EARTH

Most radiation is absorbed by the Earth's surface and warms it.

Infrared radiation is emitted from the Earth's surface.

allows less heat to escape from the atmosphere, causing temperatures to rise. A warmer climate world-wide could have several consequences for ecosystems and humans. Some scientists predict that global warming could lead to increased drought, increased flooding, loss of habitats and species, disruption of farming and food supplies, and a higher incidence of respiratory diseases and tropical diseases in humans.

Carbon dioxide is building up in the atmosphere for two reasons. First, human activities produce carbon dioxide, adding more to the atmosphere. Carbon dioxide is being added to the atmosphere by burning wood or fossil fuels. Burning coal for generating electricity, using oil to heat homes, and driving cars are major sources of carbon dioxide emissions that contribute to global warming. The second reason that the balance of the carbon cycle has been disrupted is human activities limit the amount of carbon that is removed from the atmosphere. Over the past century many acres of forest have been cleared for cities or farms. This clear-cutting of forest has been particularly significant for the tropical rainforests. Large areas of the rainforest have been cleared to make way for cattle farms. Since there are fewer trees, there is less photosynthesis occurring, using less carbon dioxide. As a result, more carbon dioxide is being returned to the atmosphere than used up. The balance of the carbon cycle has been disrupted so the level of carbon dioxide is increasing in the atmosphere.

Lesson Summary

1. Photosynthesis is the process by which green plants make their own food.

2. Green plants remove carbon dioxide from the air and supply oxygen to the air.

3. Cellular respiration is the process by which all organisms break down carbohydrates for energy.

4. Global warming is a result of too much carbon dioxide in the air.

Lesson #4 – Questions

1. Why is carbon important for living things?

_____

_____

2. Indicate whether each statement is true or false. If a statement is false, explain why.
   (a) Photosynthesis adds carbon to the atmosphere. _____

   _____

   (b) Cellular respiration uses oxygen and releases carbon dioxide. _____

   _____

   (c) When an animals dies, the carbon in its body is no longer available to the ecosystem. _____

   _____

3. Explain how carbon moves from the atmosphere into the food chain.

   _____

   _____

4. How does clearing forests upset the balance of the carbon cycle?

   _____

   _____

Lesson # 5 – The Nitrogen Cycle

Objectives:

- Explain why nitrogen is important to living things

- Describe the path that nitrogen takes through ecosystems

- Describe three roles of bacteria in the nitrogen cycle

- Describe three effects of excess nitrogen in the environment

Nitrogen Cycle

If you have ever had a vegetable garden, you may have used fertilizers to improve your crop. Fertilizers contain nutrients that help plants grow. One of the main ingredients of fertilizers is nitrogen. Nitrogen, one of the most common elements, is essential for the formation of proteins, DNA, and other important molecules. By fertilizing your garden, you are supplying the plants with a lot of nitrogen. In this way, the plants can build more proteins, producing more vegetables. More fertilizer is added throughout the growing season to replenish the supply of nitrogen in the soil. In natural ecosystems, though, new nitrogen is not added to the soil. Instead, the nitrogen that plants use is recycled and reused over and over again. Nitrogen cycles through the ecosystem in a way similar to carbon. Nitrogen is absorbed from the environment by plants, passed through the food chain, and eventually returned to the physical environment.

The nitrogen cycle will be explained in detail during this lesson. (See the diagram on the next page.)

Nitrogen Fixation

The major source of nitrogen in ecosystems is the atmosphere. Although nitrogen gas makes up almost 80% of the atmosphere, we still use fertilizers to supply plants with this important nutrient. Fertilizers are used because most organisms cannot use the nitrogen gas that is found in the atmosphere. The nitrogen gas must be changed or fixed into different forms before it can be absorbed by plants. In the process of nitrogen fixation, specialized bacteria transform nitrogen gas into ammonia and nitrates. Ammonia and nitrates are nitrogen compounds which are easily absorbed by the roots of plants. The bacteria that accomplish this task are called nitrogen fixing bacteria. These bacteria, found in the soil and water, act

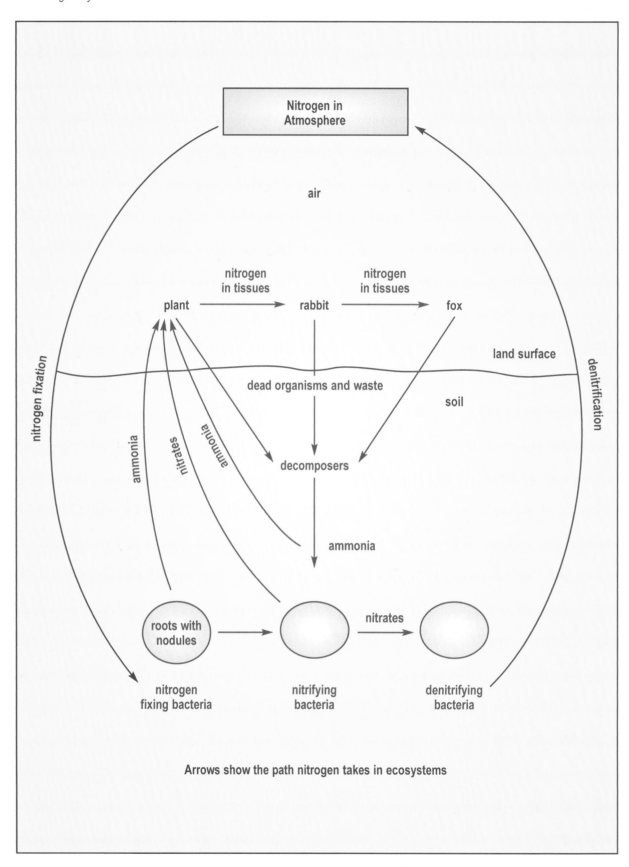

Arrows show the path nitrogen takes in ecosystems

on the nitrogen gas in the atmosphere, changing it into the form plants can use. The resulting nitrates and ammonia are deposited in the soil and water, ready to be absorbed by the roots of a plant. A common nitrogen fixing bacteria is Rhizobia and is found in the nodules on the roots of leguminous plants such as peas, clover, beans, and alfalfa. Farmers plant these crops as a way of providing a usable form of nitrogen to the soil. In aquatic ecosystems, the cyanobacteria fix nitrogen. Lightning is also responsible for some nitrogen fixation.

 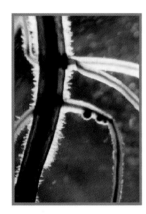

Nodules on Roots

Nitrogen fixation is a key process in the nitrogen cycle: it allows nitrogen to enter the food chain. Once the nitrogen compounds are absorbed by the plants, the plant uses the nitrogen for the formation of protein and DNA. Now the nitrogen is available to the other organisms through the food chain. When a plant is consumed, the nitrogen stored in its tissues is passed to the next level of the food chain. As with carbon, the nitrogen continues to move through the food chain as one animal consumes another. This is important because all organisms need nitrogen to survive and animals can only get nitrogen by consuming plants or animals that have eaten plants.

Completing the Nitrogen Cycle

To complete the nitrogen cycle, the nitrogen supplies in the atmosphere and the soil must be replenished. First, waste and dead organisms contain nitrogen that can be recycled and reused. Decomposer bacteria break down dead organisms, releasing ammonia into the soil and water as a by-product. Ammonia is a compound of nitrogen and hydrogen. Some plants will absorb the ammonia, recycling nitrogen into the food chain. The ammonia is also converted into nitrates by nitrifying bacteria. The process of converting ammonia into nitrates is called nitrification. The resulting nitrates can be absorbed by other plants. Finally nitrogen must be returned to the atmosphere. Yet another set of bacteria, called the denitrifying bacteria, convert the nitrates into nitrogen gas in a process called denitrification. The nitrogen in the atmosphere will then be cycled once again through ecosystems, starting with the nitrogen fixing bacteria. The work of different bacteria cycles the nitrogen from the atmosphere to the soil, through the food chains and back to the soil and atmosphere again.

Human Activities and the Nitrogen Cycle

Maintaining the balance of the nitrogen cycle is important to the health of the ecosystem. The nitrogen that is removed by plants from the environment should be roughly equivalent to the amount of nitrogen that is added to the environment. Several human activities have upset the balance by adding nitrogen to the ecosystem. Farming is one of these activities. Fertilizers contain industrial fixed nitrogen. Fertilizer use has added large amounts of nitrogen to soil. Industrial activities also add nitrogen to the ecosystem because burning fossil fuels releases nitrogen compounds into the atmosphere. Twenty-five million tons of nitrogen compounds are released from vehicles, power plants and industry in the United States each year. All of these activities can overload an ecosystem with nitrogen. There are consequences for the soil, air, and water.

Excess nitrogen in the soil creates an acidic environment that damages tree roots and stunts growth. One telltale sign of this damage is that the needles on spruce trees turn yellow. In the atmosphere, the nitrogen compounds contribute to acid rain, which affects the health of forests and upsets aquatic ecosystems. Many lakes, particularly in the north-eastern United States and Canada are now too acidic to support fish because of acid rain. Even farms are hurt by acid rain. The acidic water that drains through the soil washes away essential nutrients such as calcium and potassium.

Acid rain is not the only way in which lakes are affected by excess nitrogen. Excess nitrogen also enters lakes through run-off that carries nitrates from farms or cities. This build up of nutrients is called eutrophication. You may think that having a lot of available nutrients is a good thing for an ecosystem, but eutrophication can have disastrous effects on a lake. When there is a lot of nitrogen in a lake, the plants in the lake grow rapidly and abundantly, forming a thick blanket. This blanket blocks the sun to the lower levels of the lake, preventing photosynthesis from occurring. As a result, the plants under the surface of the water die, and stop producing oxygen. As more and more plants die, the decomposers in the lake are able to thrive on all of the decaying matter. These decomposers use oxygen, so more and more oxygen is removed from the lake. The oxygen levels in the lake become so low that many fish and animals die.

Lesson Summary

1. Fertilizers contain nitrogen and other nutrients that help plants grow.

2. Nitrogen fixation allows nitrogen from the atmosphere to enter the food chain.

3. Plants use nitrogen for the formation of protein and DNA.

4. Excess nitrogen in the soil creates an acidic environment which stunts plant growth.

5. Excess nitrogen contributes to acid rain.

Notes

_____

_____

_____

_____

_____

_____

_____

_____

_____

_____

_____

_____

_____

_____

_____

_____

_____

_____

_____

Lesson #5 – Questions

1. Match each of the following terms with the correct definition.

Nitrogen fixation _____

Eutrophication _____

Denitrification _____

Ammonia _____

Rhizobia _____

    (a) a build up of nutrients in a lake that causes rapid plant growth and oxygen depletion

    (b) the process by which nitrogen gas in the atmosphere is converted to a nitrogen compound that can be used by plants

    (c) a nitrogen fixing bacteria

    (d) a nitrogen compound that is easily absorbed by the roots of some plants

    (e) the process by which nitrates in the soil are converted to nitrogen gas

2. Why are nitrogen fixing bacteria important to the nitrogen cycle?

_____

_____

_____

_____

3. How does the nitrogen in a dead organism return to the atmosphere?

_____

_____

_____

_____

Lesson #6 – Other Nutrient and Life Cycles

Objectives:

- Describe how phosphorus is cycled through ecosystems

- Give two examples of how human activity has disrupted the phosphorus cycle

- Explain in genera terms how nutrients are cycled through ecosystems

- Describe how water is cycled through ecosystems

- Describe how the water cycle is disrupted by human activities

Phosphorus Cycle

You have learned about the carbon and nitrogen cycles. In both of these cycles, the nutrient is cycled between the atmosphere and the food chain. However, many nutrients are not found in the atmosphere, but in the bedrock that is part of the Earth's crust. Phosphorus is one of these nutrients. Phosphorus is a limiting factor for plant growth. This means that if there were more phosphorus present, plants would be more productive. Since most soils are low in phosphorus, fertilizers are commonly used to encourage plant growth. Plants need phosphorus to grow, as do the animals that eat the plants. Phosphorus is necessary for building nucleic acids, cell membranes and bones and teeth. Like any other nutrient, phosphorus is in limited supply in ecosystems and must be recycled and reused.

The phosphorus cycle follows the same general pattern as the nitrogen and carbon cycles. Like carbon and nitrogen, phosphorus is cycled from the environment through the food chain, and back to the environment again. However, there is one major difference. Whereas the nitrogen and carbon are taken from the atmosphere and then cycled through the ecosystem, phosphorus is taken from rock. We will learn how this affects how a nutrient is cycled in an ecosystem.

The phosphorus cycle begins when the action of wind, water, and changing temperatures starts to break down rocks through the weathering process. Weathering slowly breaks apart rocks, forming smaller and smaller pieces. Eventually, these pieces of weathered rock make up a part of the soil. The soil will contain any nutrients that are found in the rock, including phosphorus. Once the phosphorus is weathered from the rocks into the soil, it is easily absorbed by the roots of plants. The plants do not need the help of bacteria as they do with nitrogen. Once incorporated into the plant, the phosphorus moves through the food chain as one organism consumes the next. The phosphorus is returned to the soil through the work of decomposers. Decomposers break down waste and dead organisms, releasing any remaining phosphorus into the soil.

Now the phosphorus begins a long journey back into the rock. Rainfall and runoff sweeps the phosphorus from the soils into lakes and oceans. Over the years, the phosphorus starts to settle to the bottom of the lakes and oceans, and becomes a part of the sediments. The pressure from the ocean compresses the sediments, forming rock. The phosphorus is now locked into the rock and will only be released once that rock is exposed and weathered. Since the phosphorus has to

be removed from and returned to rock, phosphorus moves very slowly through ecosystems when compared to nitrogen and carbon. It would take longer than your lifetime for a phosphorus atom to complete its cycle.

Human Activities and the Phosphorus Cycle

When phosphorus containing compounds such as fertilizers are added to the environment, the balance of the phosphorus cycle is upset. Ideally, the amount of phosphorus being added to the ecosystem should equal the amount of phosphorus that is being taken out of the ecosystem. By adding fertilizer, farmers and gardeners are increasing the amount of phosphorus in the ecosystem. Other sources of excess phosphates are animal wastes from livestock and the discharge of municipal sewage. Most of the excess

The Phosphorus Cycle

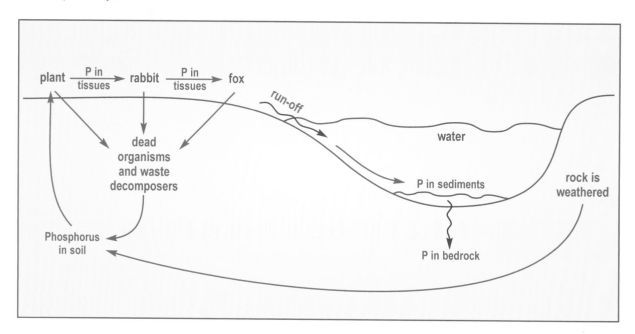

phosphate from different human sources is washed into the lakes and oceans. Phosphorus builds up in the lakes and rivers, leading to the eutrophication of the lake in some cases. Phosphate levels are also decreased by human activities. Phosphate containing rocks are mined for use in fertilizers and detergents. When these rocks are removed from an ecosystem, there is less potential for phosphorus to enter the soil. Phosphorus levels are also reduced when tropical forests are cut to make room for farms or settlements. Once all of the vegetation is cleared away, the soil is left exposed to the heavy rains that are typical of tropical climates. These heavy rains wash away the phosphorus and other nutrients in the soil.

We have looked at a few examples of nutrient cycles. These three examples are enough to illustrate how most nutrients are cycled. This is because the nutrients follow the same general pattern of moving from the biotic to the abiotic components of an ecosystem. In the ecosystem, there is a reservoir for the nutrients, whether it is the atmosphere, the ocean, or the earth's crust. The nutrient is absorbed by a plant and moves through the food chain as one organism consumes another. All of the waste and dead organisms along the way also contain the nutrient. You can think of the dead organisms and waste as a package of nutrients. Decomposers open that package, returning the nutrients to the environment. So in nutrient cycles, chemical elements are always moving from the abiotic part of the ecosystem to

the biotic part and back again. Also, death and decomposition are essential. A dead organism becomes the site of much activity as the decomposers release nutrients to the ecosystem. In this way nutrients are recycled and then available for reuse. These cycles have been repeating themselves since life began on Earth. So imagine, the carbon in your bones was once part of a carbon dioxide molecule in the atmosphere but was also part of many other organisms before that.

Water Cycle

Water also cycles through ecosystems. You may have noticed that water plays a role in nutrient cycles by carrying nutrients from place to place or by dissolving nutrients so they can be absorbed by plants. This is only one of the reasons that water is essential to life. In addition to dissolving different substances to be used by organisms, water performs several vital functions. Water is a basic component of all living tissues. Your own body is mostly water. In fact, water makes up about 70% of the body's of living things. Water also helps to maintain body temperatures and provides a medium for chemical reactions within organisms. In short, all organisms depend on water to survive.

The water cycle is the simplest nutrient cycle. As water moves through the ecosystem, most of it remains as water and is not used to make new molecules for plants and animals. The water cycle simply collects and redistributes water throughout the ecosystems. The water source for all ecosystems is the oceans. Ninety-seven per cent of Earth's available water is contained by oceans. Throughout the water cycle, water is removed from the ocean, distributed to different ecosystems and eventually returned to the ocean. The two main processes that move water in the water cycle are evaporation and precipitation. Evaporation, the conversion of water into water vapor, is powered by solar energy. Evaporation can occur from the oceans or from the land. When water evaporates from the surface of plants, the term transpiration is used. The evaporated water condenses (changes from water vapor to droplets of water) and collects in clouds in the atmosphere. Climatic conditions determine when gravity returns the water to the Earth's surface through precipitation. The precipitation can fall as rain, sleet, hail, etc. Most of the water in the water cycle evaporates from the ocean and returns directly back to the ocean through precipitation. Comparatively small amounts of water evaporate from land.

The water that falls on land takes many different routes back to the ocean. Run off occurs when water moves along the surface of the Earth and drains back into the ocean. Some water is absorbed by the ground, moving into the soil and then into the groundwater. The groundwater is water that is stored in pores and cracks of rocks. Eventually the groundwater drains downhill through rock pores and

back into the ocean. Small amounts of the precipitation that falls on land enters the food chain. Plants absorb water through their roots, animals drink water or obtain water through eating other organisms. The water locked in plant and animal tissues returns to the environment through transpiration or cellular respiration. Remember that water is a product of cellular respiration. So as plants and animals break down carbohydrates for energy, water is released to the environment. (See the diagram on the next page.)

Human Activites and the Water Cycle

Humans need water. As the world population grows, the demand for water has increased rapidly. We use water in industry and farming as well as in a variety of ways in our homes. The demand that humans have for water is depleting the world's freshwater supply. In the parts of the world where human demand on the water supply is coupled with a hot dry climate, clean freshwater is becoming scarce. There are several ways to increase the freshwater supply. These include building dams and reservoirs to collect and store runoff, withdrawing groundwater, and desalination, converting saltwater to freshwater. All of these methods have successfully supplied different populations with more freshwater. However, each of these strategies also have negative effects on ecosystems and the water cycle. Dams form reservoirs that flood surrounding ecosystems, while reducing the water flow in the part of the river after the dam. In some cases the water in the river becomes so limited that it fails to reach the ocean as part of the water cycle. Withdrawing groundwater also disrupts the water cycle. Desalination produces large amounts of waste water containing high levels of salt. This waste must be absorbed by ecosystems.

Diagram Summarizes the Water Cycle

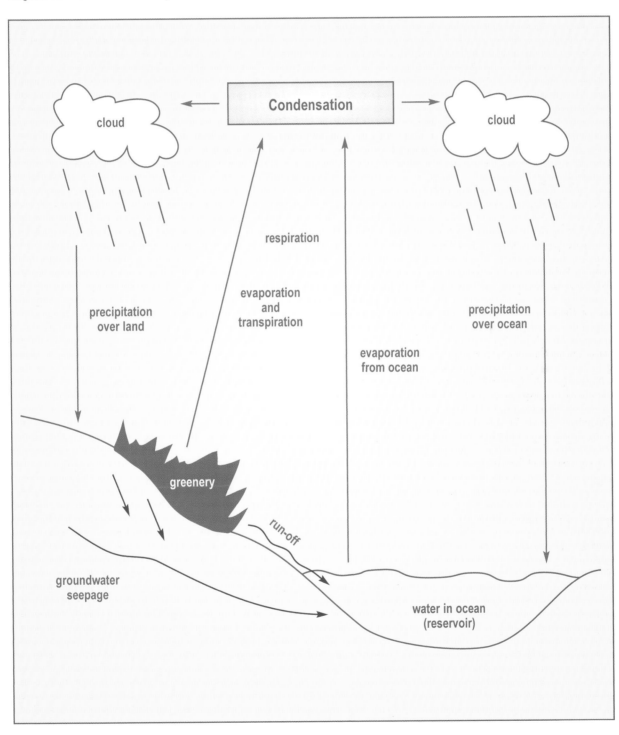

Lesson #6 – Questions

1. (a) How is the phosphorus cycle different from the nitrogen and carbon cycle?

_____

_____

_____

_____

(b) How does the above difference affect the rate at which phosphorus is cycled through the ecosystem?

_____

_____

_____

_____

2. (a) Name three ways in which humans add phosphorus to ecosystems.

_____

_____

_____

_____

Lesson #6 – Questions (continued)

(b) What is a consequence of excess phosphorus in ecosystems?

_____

_____

_____

3. Most nutrient cycles follow the same general pattern. Draw a diagram that shows how nutrients are cycled by putting each of the following events in the correct order.

- Decomposers break down dead organisms and waste
- Nutrient in atmosphere or rock
- Nutrient moves through food chain
- Nutrient absorbed by plant
- Nutrient released to atmosphere or rock

Lesson #6 – Questions (continued)

4. Once water evaporates from the ocean, describe 3 different routes the water can take to return to the ocean.

_____

_____

_____

_____

_____

_____

5. Name three ways in which human activities disrupt the water cycle.

_____

_____

_____

_____

_____

_____

_____

Notes

_____

_____

_____

_____

_____

_____

_____

_____

_____

_____

_____

_____

_____

Interactions Between Climate, Soil and Organisms

Lesson #7 – The Importance of Climate and Soil

Objectives:

• Define the concept of climate

• Describe the characteristic of soil

• Explain why soil is important in an ecosystem

• Describe how climate, soil, and organisms interact in an ecosystem

You now know that when you walk through a forest, you are observing an ecosystem. As you walk through that forest, you may notice many different populations of plants and animals. These populations are continually interacting with each other and the environment. You have learned that these interactions form food chains and are supported by energy flow and nutrient cycles. If you then visited a grassland, you would immediately notice that many of the plants and animals are much different. However, the interactions that are occurring would be the same. Food chains are formed, energy flows and nutrients are cycled. Then why is one ecosystem different from the next? This question can be answered when we take a closer look at the abiotic factors in an ecosystem, namely the climate and

soil. The climate and soil play important roles in determining what life can exist in an area. The interactions that occur between organisms, climate, and soil shape the character of each ecosystem.

Climate

Climate is the average weather conditions of an area over many years. When you know the climate of an area, you know what the typical weather conditions might be at a certain time of year. For example, you would expect hot humid weather in the summer in New York. Winter in Minnesota would mean cold and dry weather. Factors that contribute to climate are latitude, elevation, and proximity to the ocean.

Regions in the same latitude tend to have the same climate. For instance, the areas near the equator have warm and humid climates. However, if you compared a mountainous region near the equator to a lowland area of the same latitude, you would find that the area of higher elevation has a cooler climate. Finally being near an ocean also influences climate. Seattle, Washington has a milder winter than Grand Forks, North Dakota. Although these two cities are at roughly the same latitude, the fact that Seattle is on the Pacific coast moderates its climate.

Although there are several elements that make up the climate of a region, rainfall and temperature are the two most important factors. Together, these factors determine growing conditions over large geographical areas. Organisms need certain temperatures to survive. Since most organisms cannot control body temperature precisely, the temperature of an area limits which organisms can survive in an ecosystem Some plants may be adapted to survive in very cold temperatures whereas other plants only thrive in warmer climates. The same holds true for rainfall. Some plants need a lot of moisture to survive whereas other plants do well in dry conditions. Since animals depend on plants for food and shelter, the kind of vegetation in an area influences what types of animals live in that area. So the climate influences what kind of ecosystem exists in different geographic regions.

The Importance of Soil

Any gardener knows that good soil is a key element for success of the crop. We will often add fertilizers or buy soil mixes to improve the chances of having a productive garden. By adding nutrients to the soil or changing the composition of the soil, a gardener hopes to have healthier plants and more vegetables. Soil is equally important in any ecosystem. The soil characteristics affect plant growth and subsequently all other organisms in the ecosystem. Some soils hold water better than others. Some soils have more nutrients than others. Both water and nutrients are important for plant growth. Also, the soil texture and depth may influence how easily a plant can take hold in an area. Since plants depend on soil for water and nutrients, as well as to anchor their roots, the soil is important in determining which plants may survive in an ecosystem.

The Characteristics of Soil

Soil is the material that covers land. You might think of soil as just dirt, but it is really a complex mixture of living and non-living things that has taken many years to form. If you took a very close look at soil, you would see a mixture of particles of weathered rock, decaying plant and animal matter, water, air spaces, and billions of living things. This mixture is organized in a series of vertical layers or horizons. Each horizon has a distinct texture and composition.

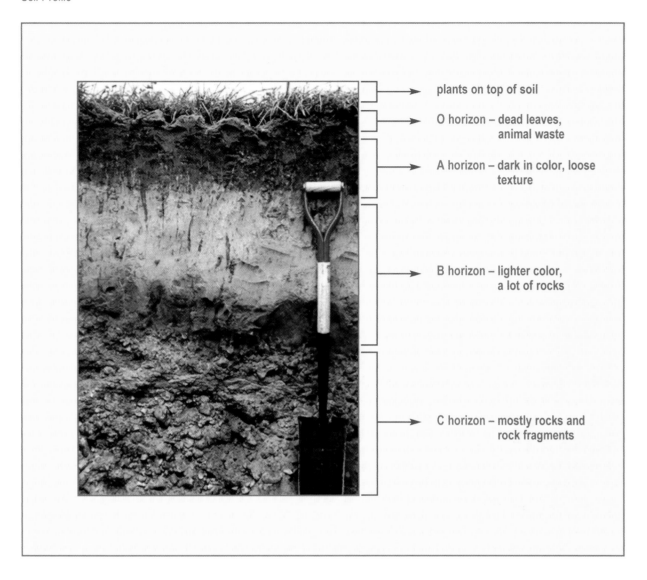

plants on top of soil

O horizon – dead leaves,
animal waste

A horizon – dark in color, loose
texture

B horizon – lighter color,
a lot of rocks

C horizon – mostly rocks and
rock fragments

The "O" or organic horizon is made up of organic matter. Freshly fallen leaves or other plant material, along with animal waste and dead parts are found at the top of the horizon. As we move further down this layer, these materials become slightly more decomposed.

The "A" horizon or topsoil consists of the decayed organic material or humus. This dark soil layer has a loose texture that holds water.

The "B" horizon or the subsoil is lighter in colour and consists of mostly inorganic material. This layer contains a lot of rocks and clay.

The "C" horizon contains fragments of rock. These fragments are pieces of the parent material, or underlying bedrock, that have worn away over long periods of time. The actions of wind and water on exposed rock as well as freezing and thawing water in the cracks of the rock work to weather or break down the rock.

The characteristics of the soil vary from one area to another. Climate and vegetation, as well as the underlying rock on which the soil forms, influence the depth, texture, and nutrient richness of the soil layers. For example, there are relatively few plants in a desert ecosystem. As a result, there is little decomposition and a thin layer of topsoil. In contrast, grassland soils have a deep topsoil. There are many plants and other organisms that decompose and contribute to the formation of a thicker topsoil. The nutrient richness of a soil varies with the bedrock. Soils that form on top of granite are nutrient poor because granite is a hard rock that does not weather and release nutrients easily. On the other hand, soils on limestone tend to have more nutrients, since limestone is easily weathered.

Microorganisms in the Soil

Soil is also the home to a busy community of microorganisms and animals. Some of these organisms are decomposers. As you know, these decomposers play an important role in nutrient cycling. Beetles, earthworms, fungi and bacteria work below the surface of the soil, decomposing waste and dead animal matter and releasing nutrients into the soil. Nitrifying and denitrifying bacteria are also found in the soil, playing an essential role in cycling nitrogen. The animals and microorganisms also form a food chain, with one organism feeding on another. All of this activity moves the soil particles around, creating spaces for the movement of air and water.

As you can see, the soil characteristics are determined by many factors. The parent material, climate, and organisms in the ecosystem all contribute to the characteristics of the soil. It may take over 200 years of decomposition and weathering to form the soil. Then, once formed, the soil continues to change. The climate can change the soil. Rainfall and wind can carry away parts of the soil, or add sediment to the soil. Hot days can dry out the soil. The organisms change the soil by adding or taking up nutrients. Organic matter is continually added to soil as organisms leave waste or die. These interactions between the climate, organisms and soil are important to ecosystems. The interactions between climate and soil shape an ecosystem and determine which plants and animals can survive in that area. Furthermore, organisms depend on soil, but they also add to it. The interactions between organisms and the soil further develop the character of an ecosystem.

Lesson Summary

1. Climate is the average weather conditions of an area over many years.

2. Rainfall and temperature are the two most important factors that make up the climate of an area.

3. Soil is a complex mixture of living and non-living things.

4. The interactions between climate and soil determine which plants and animals can survive in the area.

Notes

_____

_____

_____

_____

_____

_____

_____

_____

_____

_____

_____

_____

_____

_____

_____

_____

_____

_____

_____

_____

_____

_____

Lesson #7 – Questions

1. Define climate.

_____

_____

_____

_____

_____

2. List four different things you might find in a handful of soil.

_____

_____

_____

_____

_____

3. What role does soil play in an ecosystem?

_____

_____

_____

_____

_____

4. Describe two ways in which microorganisms affect the characteristics of the soil.

_____

_____

_____

_____

_____

Lesson #8 – Adaptation and Biodiversity

Objectives:

• Define adaptation

• Describe four examples of adaptation

• Define biodiversity and explain why biodiversity is important to an ecosystem

• List the ways in which humans affect biodiversity

Adaptation

Climate and soil influence which organisms can survive in an area. Each population in an ecosystem has special tools and strategies to survive under specific environmental conditions. For example, the plants in the desert have very different characteristics than the plants in the rainforest. The soil and climate of each of these regions create conditions in which plants develop specific tools to survive. In the desert, there is very little rainfall. Cacti can survive in such dry conditions because they can store water. In addition, cacti have modified leaves or spines through which they could lose water. The conditions in a rainforest are entirely different. The dark humid conditions lead to different vegetation. Tropical plants typically have large broad leaves that can collect ample sunlight for photosynthesis. The large surface of the leaves also allows the plant to radiate heat during hot weather. A cactus can survive the harsh desert conditions, but if you transplanted the cactus to the rainforest it would not survive. Similarly, a tropical plant would not survive in the desert. This is because each plant is adapted to its own specific environment, but does not have the characteristics to survive in another environment. Organisms that are adapted to where they live have tools and strategies that allow them to cope better with certain environmental conditions. In other words, in order to survive, organisms must be suited to how and where they live.

Each of the five birds pictured are adapted to their specific environments. You will notice that the bills of these birds are quite different in shape. Each of the bills is specially adapted for the kind of food that the bird eats. The **sandpiper** lives along the seashore. It has a long thin beak that is adapted for picking insects out of the sand. The **cardinal**, an inhabitant of the forest, has a triangular beak that is good for cracking open seeds. The pelican, another bird that lives by the sea, has a long large bill with a pouch of skin under the lower beak. The **pelican** snatches fish from the ocean with its long bill and then stores the fish in its pouch. The pelican can then consume the fish at its leisure or save the fish to feed to its young. The **hummingbird** has a bill that is adapted for feeding on flower nectar. The bill is a long thin tube that can reach into flowers. Different species of hummingbirds have different sizes of bills, depending on the shape of the flowers they feed on. The **golden eagle** preys on small mammals. Its large, hooked bill allows it to hold onto and tear apart its prey. Each of these strategies for feeding allows the birds to compete successfully for food and survive in their environments.

pelican

golden eagle

All organisms in all ecosystems are adapted to their environments. Otherwise, the organism would not survive. These adaptations provide plants and animals with special strategies for finding shelter, hiding from prey, finding a mate, reproducing, as well as finding food. As populations of organisms become adapted to their environments, many different strategies and tools develop. In this way, the process of adaptation, which occurs over generations of an organism, leads to a wide variety of plants and animals.

Biodiversity

Biodiversity is a measure of the variety of species on Earth. There is a large diversity of plants and animals on Earth because different environmental conditions lead to different adaptations. Some regions of the Earth have more biodiversity than others. Regions that are subject to extreme conditions such as very hot or very cold weather tend to have fewer varieties of plants and animals. When the conditions are extreme only a few species of plants are able to adapt to these conditions. A small variety of plants only attracts a small variety of animals. Thus, ecosystems such as deserts or Arctic areas have less

cardinal

hummingbird

sandpiper

biodiversity than temperate forests and tropical rainforests.

The variety of species in an area make up a community. These organisms live in that community in order to meet their special needs. Biodiversity is important in a community and its ecosystem because having a variety of organisms ensures the success of all living things. In your own community, you depend on a variety of people to meet your needs. You depend on people to produce your food, build your home, or provide transportation. At the same time you provide goods or services to your community through the work that you do, your activities in the neighborhood, supporting businesses when you shop, or by raising your children. The people in your community have special roles that contribute to the functioning of that community. The same holds true for an ecosystem. A diversity of organisms in an ecosystem performs many different jobs for the functioning of the ecosystem. A variety of trees, grasses and plants provide different kinds of shelter for different animals. The diverse plant and animal life are food sources for many different animals. Some animals may help populations by preying on the weak members of that population. Different animals and microorganisms decompose different waste and dead organisms to release nutrients. These are only a small number of the ways that biodiversity provides for a successful ecosystem. The interrelationships in an ecosystem are complex and depend upon a large variety of organisms, each with their own job.

There is concern that human activities are affecting biodiversity. A diverse ecosystem is considered a healthy one, but human activities are contributing to the extinction or endangerment of many species. Many ecosystems are destroyed to benefit human activities such as agriculture and housing. The loss of habitat through the clearing of forests and draining of wetlands has led to the loss of many species. Plants and animals that no longer have a place to live cannot survive. Also, the biodiversity of intact ecosystems is being affected. Some of the factors that have affected the biodiversity of ecosystems are pollution, over-fishing, hunting, or the sale of exotic pets. Each of these activities reduces the numbers of a specific species in an ecosystem. Since each species has a special job in the ecosystem, its extinction or endangerment has consequences for the entire ecosystem.

For instance, at one time, the gray wolf was hunted to near extinction, with the goal of safeguarding livestock and big game animals. The wolf's jobs in the ecosystem included keeping down elk, moose, and coyote populations by hunting them and providing uneaten meat for scavengers such as ravens and bald eagles. As the wolf population declined, vegetation was depleted by larger numbers of elk and moose, the food supply for eagles and ravens was limited, and farmers were concerned about the growing population of coyotes. This example illustrates the importance of maintaining biodiversity in an ecosystem, since each species has an important role in an ecosystem.

Lesson Summary

1. In order to survive, organisms have to be able to adapt to their surroundings.

2. Biodiversity is a measure of the variety of species on Earth.

3. A diverse ecosystem is a healthy ecosystem.

Lesson #8 – Questions

1. Indicate whether each statement is true or false. If the statement is false, explain why.

(a) Organisms can easily move from one type of ecosystem to another. _____

_____

(b) More extreme climates have higher biodiversity. _____

_____

(c) Ecosystems depend on a variety of plants and animals to survive. _____

_____

(d) A large broad plant leaf is an adaptation to low light conditions. _____

_____

2. Explain why the sandpiper's long thin bill is an adaptation. _____

_____

_____

3. List four human activities that affect biodiversity. _____

_____

_____

Lesson #9 – Establishing an Ecosystem: Succession and Biomes

Objectives:

- List the typical steps that occur during primary succession

- Define climax community

- Describe an example of secondary succession

- Define the term biome

- Give examples of biomes and describe how the climate has influenced vegetation and animal life in those biomes

Succession

Changes in environmental conditions are always occurring. Some of these changes, such as a forest fire or a tornado are obvious. Other changes are more subtle, such as more moisture or shade developing in a forest. Since organisms must be adapted to the environment to survive, these changes must lead to changes in the communities that live there. In the previous lesson you learned about some of the adaptations birds have for getting their food. Although each of these birds is well adapted to its environment, their survival would be threatened if the environment changed. For instance the flower variety that a species of hummingbird feeds on could die out because of disease. Since the bird's beak is specially adapted for that particular variety of flower the hummingbird either has to move to another ecosystem where that flower is available or adapt to the new food supply. Otherwise, the hummingbird species would die.

When the environment changes, all organisms are faced with the same dilemma. Some organisms may die, some organisms may move, and some organisms, over the period of many years and many generations, may change. As a result, ecosystems as a whole change over time in response to changes in the environment. Ecosystems are always changing. This means that the field at the outskirts of your community may have once been bare rock or a lake. Furthermore, you could return to that field and notice that over time, the ecosystem has continued to change. In many years, that field could develop into a forest. Trees have replaced the grasses and shrubs that were once there. This process of change in ecosystems in which one community of organisms replaces another is called succession. Through succession, a field may develop into a forest or a lake into a marsh.

Primary Succession

There are two types of succession: primary succession and secondary succession.

Primary succession occurs when an ecosystem develops from scratch. That is, an ecosystem forms, over a long period of time, on the surface of bare rock. The precise changes that occur during primary succession vary according to the environment (climate, type of rock), but the same general stages are the same.

1. The bare rock that starts this process could be a result of erosion, a retreating glacier, or cooling lava. Even an abandoned road could be the site of primary succession. Over time, the bare rock is weathered. The action of water freezing and thawing causes cracks to form in the rock.

2. As the cracks form, lichens are able to colonize on the rocks. These plants are referred to as pioneer organisms. You can imagine that the pioneers who settled in North America had to be tough to survive their new, harsh environment. The same applies to the pioneer organisms. They are hardy invaders that can live without soil or shelter. The lichen plays an important role in creating an environment in

Primary Succession

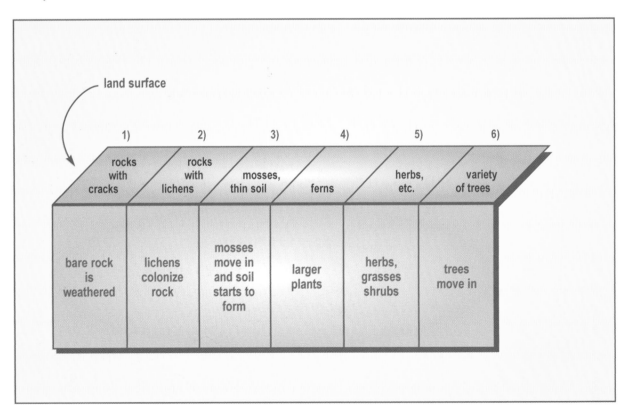

land surface

1) rocks with cracks
2) rocks with lichens
3) mosses, thin soil
4) ferns
5) herbs, etc.
6) variety of trees

bare rock is weathered | lichens colonize rock | mosses move in and soil starts to form | larger plants | herbs, grasses shrubs | trees move in

which other plants can colonize the rock. Lichens have acid secretions which dissolve the rock. In this way the minerals in the rock become available for use by other plants.

3. Mosses then move in. Together the moss and lichen trap windblown particles, helping matter to accumulate for the formation of soil. The moss and lichen that may die off will decay and contribute to soil formation. Also, these plants trap water. Slowly, conditions on the rock are becoming more favorable for other organisms. A thin soil has formed and the rock is developing more and more cracks.

4. The soil attracts insects and other soil organisms that aid in the decomposition of organic matter. The soil begins to accumulate in the cracks of the rock, and more moisture can collect. The environment has become favorable for larger plants such as ferns. As more plants grow on the once bare rock, the changes begin to occur faster, allowing even more plants to grow.

5. Eventually, herbs, grasses and low shrubs move in, their seeds having been transported by wind or animals. As these plants grow, more insects and other animals are attracted to the area. A larger community is being established, slowly replacing some of the pioneers. As conditions become shadier and damper, the sun-loving lichen dies off.

6. The soil continues to accumulate, more moisture is retained and taller and taller trees begin to grow. Each new species changes the environment, crowding out earlier colonizers. Eventually, the ecosystem becomes full. Conditions are such that a new species is unable to make its way into the area. A climax community is formed.

The climax community is the end product of succession. It can take a thousand years or more for a climax forest to develop from bare rock. If left undisturbed, the climax community will remain stable.

climax forest

Secondary Succession

Secondary succession occurs after an ecosystem is disturbed. An event such as a forest fire, a volcanic eruption, the spread of a disease, or clearing a forest can disturb an ecosystem. Communities of plants and animals are destroyed. However, these areas will eventually regenerate through the process of secondary succession. Secondary succession is the process of rebuilding an ecosystem once the original ecosystem has been disturbed. It does not start from scratch. At the very least the soil remains, if not some communities of organisms. With the disappearance of some populations, there is now space in the ecosystem for new organisms to move in. As in primary succession, one species replaces another until the climax community is formed. Since the soil is already formed, secondary succession occurs relatively quickly compared to primary succession.

clearing a forest   *volcanic eruption*

The figure on the next page illustrates the process of secondary succession after a climax forest has been ravaged by a fire. Much of the ecosystem has been destroyed. Any animals that survive move to other ecosystems since there is no longer any shelter and very little food available. The ashes from the fire enrich the original soil from the forest, so the soil that is left is nutrient rich. The first plants to move into the area are grasses and wildflowers. These plants grow quickly, profiting from the nutrient rich soil, sunny conditions and lack of competition. A meadow has formed, and as it does, the environment of the ecosystem is changing. There is more moisture and shade, creating ideal growing conditions for larger shrubs and trees. One of the first trees that may grow after a forest fire is the Jack pine. The Jack Pine has an adaptation to allow the population to survive forest fires. In the extreme heat of the fire, the Jack Pine cones release their seeds.

The trees and shrubs that have moved into the area provide new sources of food and shelter. This attracts different populations of animals to move into the ecosystem. As in primary succession, each new species alters the environment, making conditions favorable for another species and perhaps crowding out other species. Eventually the climax community is formed. The result will be similar to the original ecosystem, but there will be different species present. The ecosystem has renewed itself. In fact, forest rangers allow some natural forest fires to burn because secondary succession can be a process of renewal for ecosystems.

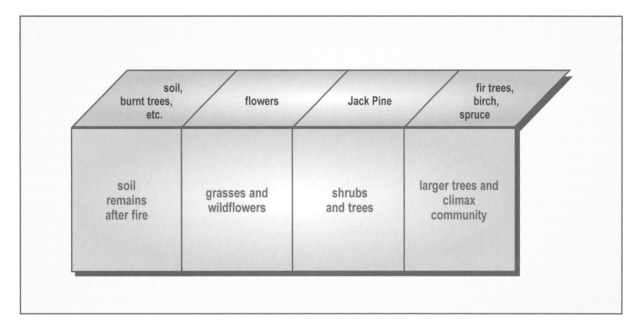

soil, burnt trees, etc.	flowers	Jack Pine	fir trees, birch, spruce
soil remains after fire	grasses and wildflowers	shrubs and trees	larger trees and climax community

Another common example of succession occurs in lakes. The changes that occur in the lake ecosystem could result from a disturbance such as an influx of nutrients or as part of the changes that occur naturally within the lake. The plants and animals that are part of a lake ecosystem will eventually die. This dead organic matter falls to the bottom of the lake and accumulates. The bottom of the lake begins to fill in and the lake becomes more shallow. Plants such as reeds and cattail begin to take hold in these shallow conditions on the edges of the lake. This new vegetation contributes even more organic matter to the lake. More matter accumulates at the bottom of the lake, building up more soil to anchor terrestrial plants. The lake becomes smaller and smaller as the vegetation starts to encroach along the edges. Eventually the lake fills in completely, forming a meadow. Over time, the meadow too, will change as the process of succession replaces the grasses and shrubs with the larger trees of a climax community.

lake succession

The next time you walk through a forest you will know that the forest has not always been there. The forest floor you are walking on may have been bare rock or a lake. This climax community has formed as a result of interactions between organisms, soil, and climate. The climate has a strong influence on the type of climax community formed. The vegetation that colonizes an area during succession must be adapted to the climatic conditions of an area. In the next section, we will examine the distinct climax communities that form over large regions with similar environmental conditions.

Biomes

If you travelled from Michigan to Costa Rica, you would notice striking differences in the landscape. You would find a different community of plants and animals, distinct from what you would find in Michigan. These distinctive communities of plants and animals are biomes. A biome is a large region that is characterized by a distinct climate and specific life forms. Each biome is a patchwork of ecosystems in which the communities have adapted to the climate and soil. As a result, regions with similar climates and topography have similar vegetation and animals. When the climate is different, the vegetation and animals are different. Biomes have been shaped by the interaction of many climatic features, but rainfall and temperature are the most important. The map shows the major biomes of the world. Biomes are named for the dominant vegetation in the area. Refer to the map as you read the following descriptions.

Biomes Map

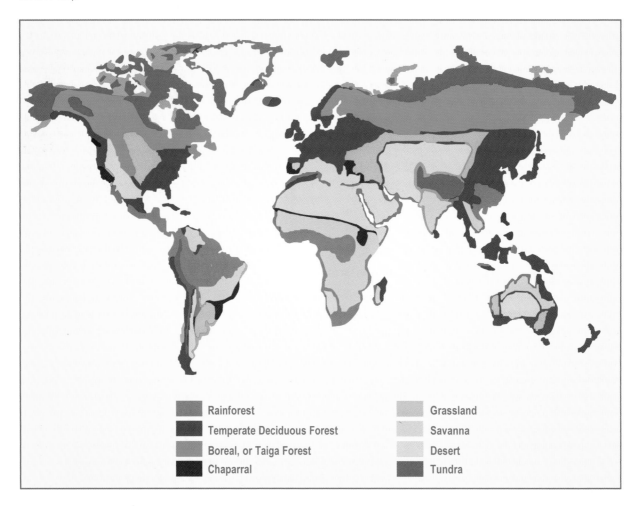

Rainforest	Grassland
Temperate Deciduous Forest	Savanna
Boreal, or Taiga Forest	Desert
Chaparral	Tundra

Tropical Rainforest

middle layers. Little sunlight reaches the forest floor, so the plants and animals that live there are limited.

Temperate Forest

Tropical rainforests are found near the equator, where day length and temperature vary little. Temperatures are warm, between 25 and 30 degrees Celsius, and the rainfall is ample. These conditions allow many different plants and animals to flourish. The tropical rainforest has the most biodiversity compared to other biomes. The trees have broad leaves and are evergreens (do not lose their leaves). As you have learned these leaves are especially adapted to deal with warm conditions and with limited sunlight on the forest floor. There are several layers of vegetation in the rainforest, with the tallest trees forming the canopy. Trees and vines of different heights form the

Temperate forests develop in the mid-latitude regions. You will find temperate forest in Eastern North America, Europe, and Asia. These regions have enough rainfall to support trees. The temperatures range from cold in the winter (-30 degrees Celsius) to hot in the summer (+35 degrees Celsius). In the cold winters, little moisture is available, and the trees have adapted by losing their leaves in the fall. Like the tropical rainforest, temperate forests have several layers, but they are much more open and not as tall. There is also a large diversity of plant and animal life. The forests support many birds, small mammals and in some cases larger predators such as wolves and mountain lions.

Taiga

Also known as coniferous forest, the taiga biome occurs in the northern regions of North America, Europe, and Asia. High altitude areas also create taiga biomes. The climate in these regions is characterized by cold winters and short cool summers. There is enough moisture to support trees, but most of the precipitation falls as snow so it is not available until everything melts in the spring. As a result the trees have adapted by being able to minimize moisture loss. The conifers or evergreens are the most common vegetation in the biome. The needles of conifers lose little water. The trees in the taiga form a dense forest, blocking out sun to lower layers. With little sunlight, only mosses, lichens, and small shrubs survive on the forest floor. Animals in the taiga include moose, squirrels, hares, beavers, grizzly bears, and lynxes.

Tundra

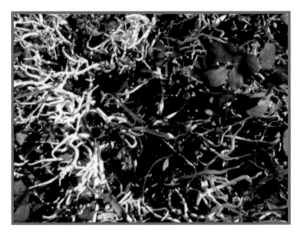

In northern latitudes and higher altitudes, the climate is such that it does not support tree growth. The arctic tundra in the northern latitudes is so cold that there is permafrost, or continuously frozen ground. The permafrost prevents plant roots from penetrating very deeply into the soil. The growing season is very short. Spring arrives in mid May and fall begins in August. Although there is little rainfall, the soil is always moist because there is little evaporation. These conditions limit what plants can survive. The vegetation in the tundra is compact and close to the ground in order to cope with cold temperatures and high winds. The vegetation is fast growing so it can reproduce within the short growing season. Grasses, mosses, lichens, and shrubs are typical of the tundra. Similar vegetation is found on alpine tundra where elevations are so high that trees cannot survive. Animals survive the cold by living in burrows, or in the case of birds, by migrating south when the temperature falls.

Grasslands

Grasslands, or prairies, are found in the middle of continents. These regions have continuous cover of grass and almost no trees. The summers are hot and dry and the winters are cold. The rainfall in grasslands is just enough to allow grasses to grow, but not enough to support the growth of trees, except in areas near streams. Although the process of succession would normally lead to grasslands developing into forests, drought and frequent fires prevent shrubs and trees from taking hold in grasslands. The grasses on the other

hand can tolerate dry conditions. Grass roots also survive fires whereas trees are completely destroyed. The soil in grasslands are fertile. With grasses decomposing over thousands of years and limited rainfall to carry away the nutrients, the topsoil is thick and nutrient rich. Grasslands are home to many grazing animals such as bison. Since the grasslands are so open, speed and endurance are important adaptations to escape predators that chase down prey. Other animals adapt by finding shelter underground or, in the case of reptiles, by camouflaging.

Desert

animals in the desert are also adapted to survive in very dry conditions. Animals such as lizards, snakes, and the kangaroo rat live in burrows and are only active at night. Smaller animals can survive without drinking water and get the water they need from cellular respiration. (Water is a product of cellular respiration). Larger animals depend on permanent water holes to survive.

Chaparral

Deserts often have very hot temperatures, but there are also cold deserts. These biomes are characterized by very little precipitation. Since conditions are so dry, plants either store water in their stems, such as the cacti, or have very small, thick, and waxy leaves to prevent water loss. Some deserts receive more rainfall than others. The drier deserts have almost no perennial (permanent) vegetation. Less arid deserts can support the growth of some shrubs and cacti. Also found in deserts are plants that can reproduce very quickly. Some plants reproduce in a matter of weeks in order to take advantage of the available moisture after a heavy rainfall. The

The chaparral or brushland biomes are found in coastal areas in Chile, southwestern Australia, California, southwestern Africa and the Mediterranean. As in the desert, plants and animals have to be able to cope with hot and dry conditions in the summer. However, cool rainy winters provide the opportunity for shrubs to grow. These shrubs have tough, spiny, waxy leaves to conserve water. The shrubs are also adapted to deal with fires. With a deep root system, the shrubs regenerate once the shrubs above them are destroyed. Other shrubs only produce seeds after a hot fire. The animals that you might find in the chaparral are deer, birds, rodents, lizards, and snakes.

Lesson Summary

1. Ecosystems are always changing.

2. Primary succession occurs when an ecosystem develops from scratch.

3. The Climax Community is the end product of succession.

4. Secondary succession occurs after an ecosystem has been disturbed by an event, such as a fire.

5. A biome is a distinct region that is characterized by a distinct climate and specific life forms.

Notes

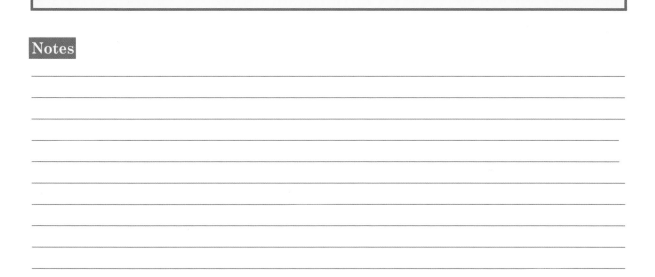

Lesson #9 – Questions

1. What is one difference between primary succession and secondary succession?

_____

_____

_____

_____

_____

_____

_____

2. Each of the following events is part of primary succession. Organize these events in the correct order.

(a) A thin soil has formed on the rock. _____

(b) Herbs, grasses, and low shrubs start to grow in the area. _____

(c) Mosses start to grow. _____

(d) Lichens grow on a bare rock. _____

(e) Larger trees take root in the ecosystem. _____

(f) A bare rock is weathered. _____

(g) Larger plants such as ferns start to grow. _____

3. Give examples of two different disturbances that would lead to secondary succession.

_____

_____

_____

_____

_____

_____

Lesson #9 – Questions (continued)

4. Complete each statement with the appropriate word or phrase.

(a) The first organisms to colonize an area during primary succession are the _____
_____
_____.

(b) A large geographic area characterized by similar climate and vegetation is a _____
_____
_____.

(c) The most biodiverse biome is the _____
_____
_____.

(d) The community that results from the process of succession is called the _____
_____
_____.

5. Name the biome in which you would find each of the following adaptations to environmental conditions.

(a) plants store water in their stems to cope with dry conditions _____
_____
_____

(b) animals need speed and endurance to escape predators in this open environment
_____
_____

(c) plants are compact and close to the ground in order to cope with high winds and cold temperatures _____
_____
_____

(d) shrubs have a deep root system so they can regenerate after a fire _____
_____
_____

Managing the Environment

Lesson #10 – Humans and Ecosystems

> **Objectives:**
>
> • List 5 ways in which humans depend on nature
>
> • Explain what an ecological footprint measures

Humans and Ecosystems

Humans depend on nature. We use land for shelter or farming. We use wood to build our homes and furniture. We use oil to fuel our cars. Our wastes are absorbed by land. We are protected from the sun's ultraviolet rays by the ozone layer in the atmosphere. We rely on ecosystems to provide many different goods and services for our basic requirements of life. As the human population on Earth continues to grow, the demands that we put on the Earth are increasing.

land for farming

wood for furniture

Human activities have affected more than 70% of the Earth's surface. In trying to meet our needs, humans have destroyed habitats, used up resources, and polluted the land, water, and air.

Tropical rainforests have been destroyed to clear land for grazing cattle. Forests in North America have been cleared to make way for urban development or farming. Seventy-five percent of fish stocks are over-fished or at the limit of over-fishing. Acid rain, resulting from air pollution, has eliminated almost all of the fish from 14,000 lakes in Canada. Enough aluminum is thrown away in the United States to rebuild the entire commercial airline fleet every three months. These activities have an enormous impact on ecosystems.

Ecosystems normally sustain themselves. There is a continuous input of energy from the sun, and the ecosystem materials are continually recycled and reused. However, human activities are disrupting ecosystems. We are using natural resources to fill our needs and polluting the environment with our wastes. The problem is that humans are not part of an ecosystem in the same way that another organism such as a fox is. A fox is limited to the food within its territory, whereas you can eat bananas or mangoes that have been imported from other countries. Foxes have to be able to cope with climatic conditions whereas you can take shelter in your homes and use heaters and air conditioners. A diseased fox is unlikely to survive whereas you can see the doctor for treatment. The food supply, climate and disease are a few of the factors that limit the fox population in an ecosystem. The ecosystem will only support so many foxes. On the other hand, human population growth has continued unchecked. In 1925, there were 2 billion people on Earth. Now, there are over 6 billion people. Humans have been able to use technology to live in high densities. The fox has adapted to fit where it lives, but you have learned to change your environment to meet your basic needs.

Ecological Footprint

We can measure the impact that humans have on ecosystems by using the ecological footprint. The ecological footprint measures how much land and water it would take to support your way of life. In order to calculate the ecological footprint of a person or a population, you must add together how much land or water you occupy, how much land or water is needed to produce the resources you use such as food or lumber, and how much land or water is needed to dispose of your wastes. The ecological footprint of a typical American is about 11 hectares. This means that it takes almost 11 hectares of land, or more than 6 city blocks, to support your lifestyle. The ecological footprint of the whole country is 3 billion hectares. It takes three times the area of the United States to support its own population. This means that Americans have to rely on ecosystems other than their own in order to meet their needs. By being able to import a large variety of goods, Americans are using the land, nutrients or biodiversity of ecosystems in other countries to support its population. Other countries find themselves in the same situation. In the Netherlands, the ecological footprint for an individual is only 5.9 hectares, but as a country the ecological footprint is 15 times the area of the country. Refer to the table on the top of the next page to see how other countries compare.

The ecological footprint is a useful measure because it shows how people are using the Earth's resources. Most countries are using more resources than what can be supplied by their own land. This is a serious situation for ecosystems. The footprint shows that the current rate of consumption of nature's goods and services will eventually use up all of the ecosystem's resources. We must learn how to manage our resources in order to preserve our resources for future generations. In other words, we need to shrink our ecological footprints.

Ecological Footprint Table

COUNTRY	HECTARES OF LAND PER PERSON
Australia	9.0
Bangladesh	0.5
Canada	7.7
Germany	5.3
India	1.0
Japan	4.3
Mexico	7.6
United States	10.9
Venezuela	3.8

Lesson Summary

1. Human activities disrupt ecosystems.

2. The "ecological footprint" measures how much land and water it would take to support your way of life.

3. Most countries use more resources than can be supplied by their own land.

4. Man must manage resources in order to preserve them for future generations.

Lesson #10 – Questions

1. List 5 ways in which humans depend on nature.

_____

_____

_____

_____

_____

_____

_____

2. Explain how a country's ecological footprint is calculated.

_____

_____

_____

_____

_____

_____

_____

_____

Notes

_____

_____

_____

_____

_____

_____

_____

_____

_____

_____

_____

_____

Lesson #11 – Managing the Environment for Future Generations

Objectives:

- Explain why we have to understand ecosystems in order to manage our environment effectively

- Explain what is meant by sustainable living

- Give two examples of sustainable practices

Managing the Environment

Humans have always tried to manage the environment to survive, but not always with success. For instance, sailors used to introduce goats to isolated oceanic islands. The goats were to serve as food once the sailors came ashore. Since the goats had no predators on the island, their population thrived. The large population of goats overgrazed these islands, killing off many of the plants. This left many of the native animals on the island without a food source. As a result these animals also died. One small change in an effort to meet the sailors' food requirements led to many changes in the ecosystem.

Another way in which we have tried to manage the environment is through the use of pesticides. These are chemicals that are designed to kill insects, but not other organisms. During World War II, the pesticide DDT was used to manage the effects of insects on humans. DDT was sprayed to control insects that carried deadly diseases, such as the mosquitoes that transmit malaria. DDT was also used on food crops to limit insect damage. Ten years later, animals in areas that had been sprayed with DDT began to die. Dead fish, frogs, and birds were discovered. These animals had high levels of DDT in their fat. Honeybees and butterflies, which are harmless and beneficial insects, disappeared. The populations of hawks, eagles, and ospreys decreased. The DDT caused these birds to produce eggs with thin shells. The eggs did not survive, and therefore the birds could not reproduce. DDT has proven to be a pesticide that stays in the environment for a long time.

When DDT is sprayed in an area, the plants become covered with the pesticide. When a primary consumer eats several plants, the DDT accumulates in that animal's fat. As one organism consumes the next, the DDT continues to accumulate in each organism. This process is called biological magnification. The result is that animals in higher trophic levels have higher levels of DDT in their body than the animals at lower trophic levels. Since DDT is passed through food chains, the pesticide was found in animals in areas that were not sprayed. DDT was also found in the tissues of humans.

The effects of spraying DDT is a good example of how we must understand how ecosystems work in order to manage our resources effectively. We know that all organisms are interconnected with each other and the environment. One small change in the ecosystem such as spraying pesticides affects many different organisms. Humans cannot avoid changing the environment, but we can choose how we change the environment to minimize the effects on ecosystems.

Sustainable Living

In order to continue to fulfil our needs and wants, we must ensure that we do not use natural resources more quickly than they can be replenished. In other words, we must live sustainably. Sustainable living means being able to satisfy our basic needs without depleting natural resources for future generations. For instance, clearing forests for our lumber needs is not a sustainable practice. Cutting down all of the trees in a forest at once is a cost effective way of producing a lot of lumber, but it is not beneficial in the long term. Although clear-cut areas are replanted with new trees, the forest will take a long time to regenerate. Also, clear-cutting reduces

biodiversity, reduces nutrient levels in the ecosystem by removing trees, and exposes the forest soil to the wind and rain, causing erosion and landslides. Clear-cutting handily meets our current needs for lumber, but it depletes the resources available to future generations. An alternative sustainable practice is selective cutting. Selective cutting involves the cutting of individual trees or small groups of trees from the forest. In this way, the forest is maintained at the same time that our needs for lumber are met. Although selective cutting is more expensive and labor intensive, this way of harvesting trees saves the forest for future generations. A healthy forest ecosystem will remain as a lumber source, a place for recreation and an important part of the biosphere. A sustainable practice balances the health of ecosystems with our needs and wants.

When we try to balance our needs with preserving ecosystems, there are many factors to consider. From the standpoint of conservation, we must evaluate how our actions affect food chains, energy flow, nutrient cycles, the soil, and biodiversity. We also must recognize that humans have certain basic needs and wants to maintain an acceptable quality of life. Our basic needs are clean air, clean water, food and shelter. In addition to these basic needs, health care, recreation, opportunity to work, education and cultural opportunities are necessary. For instance, if you were asked if allowing hunting in a park is a sustainable practice, you would probably think that it isn't. After all, you know removing one species from an area would affect many different aspects of the ecosystem. If the deer were protected, the park ecosystem would remain healthy. However, protecting an animal from hunting is not always the best way to manage the environment. If the deer were protected, the population would increase. A large deer population could damage forests because they feed on young trees and these trees are damaged and die. Ground cover and shrubs would be eaten as well, leaving the soil vulnerable to erosion and destroying the habitat of a number of songbirds. The increased deer population would affect human populations as well. Deer may end up grazing on agricultural land or causing road accidents. Also, the deer tick, which carries Lyme disease would increase in number. We would then be at greater risk of getting Lyme disease. In this case it might be wise to allow deer hunting, but with strict limits on the hunting season as well as on the number of deer that can be killed. In this way we can manage the deer population so that there are enough to maintain a healthy ecosystem, but not so many that both humans and ecosystems are negatively affected. When we consider the impact of different actions on our own lives, as well as on the ecosystem, we are better equipped to make decisions for a sustainable future.

Economics vs. Ecology

The economy is an important consideration when making decisions about managing resources. For instance,

clear-cutting forests is not a sustainable activity, but is still practiced world-wide. This is because the economic value of clear-cutting a forest takes priority over the environmental cost. It is much cheaper to clear cut a forest than to use selective cutting. Also, clear-cutting provides jobs to many people. It is sometimes difficult to choose an environmentally sustainable route when it comes at an economic cost. The same holds true for individuals. Perhaps you have decided that pesticide use should be discouraged. You plan on buying organically grown produce in order to support the farmers who have decided not to use pesticides. However, in the grocery store you realize that the organically grown produce is much more expensive. You have to decide whether or not saving ecosystems from pesticides is worth the financial sacrifice on your part.

Governments are also faced with the same kind of dilemma. In 1992, an Earth Summit was held in Rio de Janeiro, Brazil. In an effort to slow global warming, 106 nations approved a Convention on Climate Change in which developed nations agreed to reduce the emissions of carbon dioxide and other greenhouse gases. This agreement was not binding. Most nations did not reach the set goals. In 1997, a second attempt was made. Leaders from 161 countries met to negotiate a treaty called the Kyoto Accord in which developed nations were required to reduce carbon dioxide emissions. Some countries, including the United States, have refused to ratify the treaty. The American government argues that reducing carbon dioxide emissions would be too costly for the economy. In order to reduce the emissions, industries would have to slow down and jobs would be lost. The government gave the economy a higher priority than the environment. Even though global climate change is a real threat, the economic value of growing industry was chosen over the cost to the environment.

The economy is often at odds with ecology. What might be good for our wallets may not be good for the environment. So in order to live sustainably, there has to be a shift in attitudes. It is no longer sufficient to think only of the economic value of our resources. We must also consider the environmental value to the health of ecosystems and humans in the long term.

Working Towards the Future

Understanding ecosystems will help us make better decisions about how to use nature's resources wisely. Throughout this unit you have learned how our daily activities put a stress on the air, water, soil, and biodiversity of ecosystems. Our ecological footprint shows that we are not living sustainably. Our present rates of consumption and production will deplete resources for future generations. If we want to shrink our ecological footprint we need to make choices that use fewer resources and pollute less. This could mean driving a smaller, fuel-efficient car, using less energy in your home, or evaluating how many of your "wants" you can put aside. Making wise choices means that the ecosystems on which we depend will be able to support future generations.

Lesson Summary

1. Man must find ways to change the environment that will minimize the negative effects on ecosystems.

2. The economy is an important factor when making decisions about managing resources. The economy is often at odds with ecology.

3. Understanding ecology will help mankind to make better decisions with respect to proper usage of nature's resources.

Lesson #11 – Questions

1. DDT is a pesticide that was sprayed to kill specific insects. Why did this chemical have such a wide ranging effect on ecosystems?

_____

_____

_____

_____

_____

_____

2. What is sustainable living?

_____

_____

_____

_____

_____

_____

3. Explain why clear-cutting a forest is not a sustainable practice.

_____

_____

_____

_____

_____

_____

4. Explain why allowing deer hunting in a park is a sustainable practice.

_____

_____

_____

_____

_____

Have you ever wondered why spiders have eight legs, while most insects have only six? Have you ever thought about the thousands of different types of plants and animals that an ocean coral reef plays host to? Look around your neighborhood. Why does the person next door have completely different characteristics than you? In 1918-1919, the influenza epidemic killed more than twenty million people. Why is it so rare now for someone to catch this virus? Why can plants produce identical copies of themselves, while no human is exactly alike? The answer to these questions, and many more, lie in the science of biology. This module will examine the structure of the cell, the structure of DNA, cell reproduction, genetic engineering and biotechnology, as well as delve into the classification of all living organisms, paying special attention to the plant and animal kingdoms.

BIOLOGY UNIT 2

Introduction to Biology Principles

Lesson #1 – Basic Cell Operations

Objectives:

- To define the structure and function of cell membrane

- To explain why smaller cells are more efficient

- To list and explain the structure and functions of organelles

- To distinguish between prokaryotic and eukaryotic, plant and animal cells

- To describe two methods by which receptors can transmit information

- To outline the various methods that cells use to move substances in and out of the cell

- To describe how energy is produced in cells

- To understand how energy is transferred among living organisms – photosynthesis and cellular respiration

---

Introduction

We will begin our quest into the science of biology, by first examining the smallest unit of life – the cell. Often gaining a broader knowledge of a subject means delving into the details of its smaller units. For instance, it would not make sense to study chemistry without any knowledge of the atom. It certainly wouldn't seem right to study geography without first learning about the cities, countries and continents of which the world is composed. Cells make up all living organisms and on their own can carry out all of the necessary functions of life – growth, removal of waste, production of energy, communication, transportation, manufacturing and recycling of materials, and repair. In fact, many of these cell characteristics are also likely characteristics of the city or town that you live in. Throughout this lesson, we will attempt to show you that in many ways, cells operate just as a city might.

The Nature of Cells

Cells are the most basic units of life. They perform numerous functions required for life and all living organisms are made of cells, yet cells are so small we need a high-powered microscope to even see them. Why is it that something so important remains so small? The answer is efficiency – getting the most work done while expending the least energy.

In order for a cell to run efficiently, all of the important structures inside of it must be close to the cell's outer boundary, where all of the materials enter and exit the cell. Also, as a cell gets larger in size, its volume gets much bigger, while its surface area increases but not by much compared to its volume. Think about it in terms of a mega-city. As the city grows outwards from the center, the city boundaries get further away from the center of the city, therefore it becomes more difficult to oversee all of the city's activities. The people running the mega-city have a harder time directing and making decisions because they are so far from all of the action. Cells are small because they are more efficient that way.

Parts of a Cell

(a) Cell Membrane

The cell membrane is the outer boundary of the cell. The primary job of the cell membrane is to regulate the flow of materials in and out of the cell. Secondarily, the membrane also offers some protection to the inner parts of the cell. The cell membrane is just like the city limits, or the border crossings between countries. When travelling from the United States to Canada it is standard procedure to get stopped at the border and be asked a few questions about what you are bringing into the country. The cell operates in much the same way as materials pass in and out of the cell. Not everything is allowed into the cell and sometimes materials are not allowed out of the cell, depending on its needs. (See the diagram below.)

The structure of the cell membrane is the primary factor in determining what materials enter and exit the cell. The membrane is a fluid double layer of phospholipids. Each phospholipid is a molecule that has two parts: a head

Cell Membrane

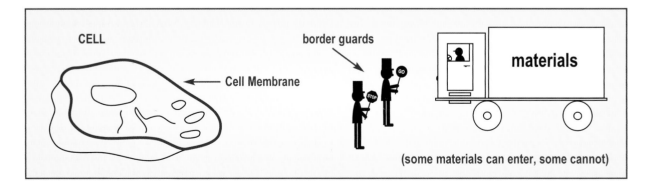

and two tails. The head contains phosphorous and nitrogen compounds and is hydrophilic, which means attracted to water. The tails are hydrophobic, which means they repel water. Because there is an abundance of water inside and outside the cell, the phospholipids arrange themselves so that the hydrophobic tails are locked on the inside of the membrane.

Single Phospholipid Molecule

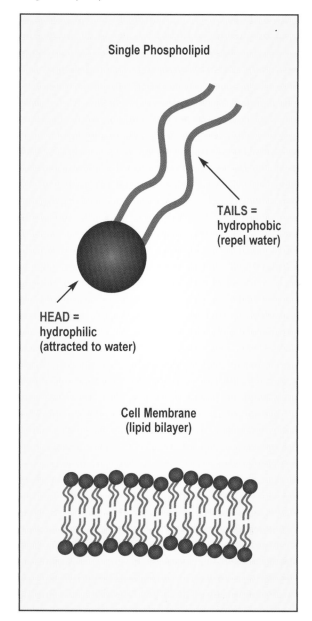

The inner, hydrophobic part of the membrane acts as a barrier to any polar molecules. Polar molecules are any molecules that have a positive and a negative end, such as water. This poses a problem for the cell, since it requires several polar molecules in order to function. As a solution to this problem, there are proteins throughout the membrane which act as channels through which polar molecules can pass. The membrane also contains other proteins which act as receptors that transmit information to the cell or as markers that identify the cell. This will be discussed later in the lesson.

Surface Proteins

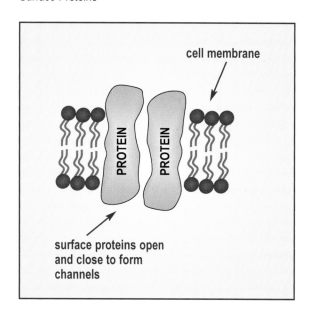

(b) Nucleus

The nucleus of the cell can be compared to city hall. It is the decision-making center of the cell and is bound by a membrane very similar to the cell membrane. This membrane controls the flow of materials into and out of the nucleus. The nucleus houses the deoxyribonucleic acid (DNA) for the cell. The DNA is formed into structures called chromosomes. The chromosomes act as the blueprint for all new cells and all cell activities. Cells with nuclei are called eukaryotic cells. Animal and plant cells all have nuclei and are therefore eukaryotic organisms.

However, not all cells have nuclei. Cells that do not have nuclei are called prokaryotic cells. For example, bacteria and viruses are prokaryotic organisms because their cells do not have nuclei.

This lesson will focus on the parts and characteristics of eukaryotic cells.

(c) Cytoplasm

The space inside the cell is filled with a liquid-like substance called cytoplasm. It fills the entire cell and is very useful at dissolving materials so that they can be transported within the cell. Also, the cytoplasm contains all of the other organelles found inside the cell. Organelles are like mini-organs that perform specialized functions in order for the cell to survive.

Eukaryotic and Prokaryotic Cells Differences

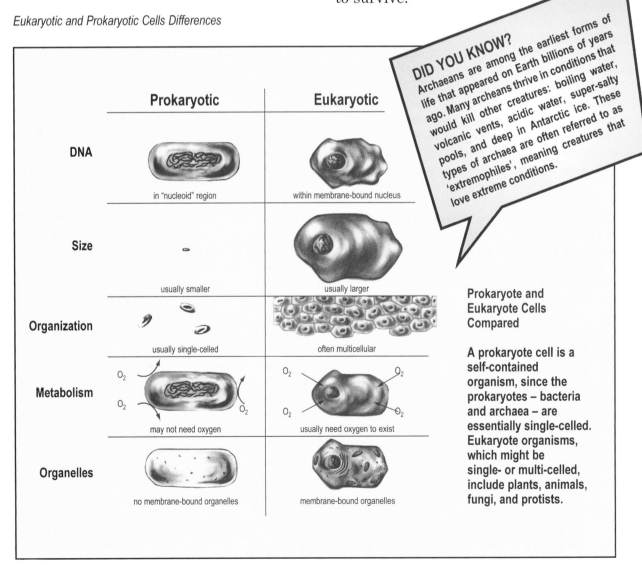

DID YOU KNOW?
Archaeans are among the earliest forms of life that appeared on Earth billions of years ago. Many archeans thrive in conditions that would kill other creatures: boiling water, volcanic vents, acidic water, super-salty pools, and deep in Antarctic ice. These types of archaea are often referred to as 'extremophiles', meaning creatures that love extreme conditions.

Prokaryote and Eukaryote Cells Compared

A prokaryote cell is a self-contained organism, since the prokaryotes – bacteria and archaea – are essentially single-celled. Eukaryote organisms, which might be single- or multi-celled, include plants, animals, fungi, and protists.

	Prokaryotic	Eukaryotic
DNA	in "nucleoid" region	within membrane-bound nucleus
Size	usually smaller	usually larger
Organization	usually single-celled	often multicellular
Metabolism	may not need oxygen	usually need oxygen to exist
Organelles	no membrane-bound organelles	membrane-bound organelles

(d) Mitochondrion

Cells require an enormous amount of energy to carry out their functions, and therefore must have a source for that energy. The mitochondrion is kidney-bean shaped and is the cell's powerhouse. It is able to extract the energy found within the chemical bonds of the food we eat and convert it into a source of energy that can be utilized by the cell. Depending upon the needs of a particular cell, there may be varying numbers of mitochondria per cell. For instance, heart muscle cells require large amounts of energy, so they have increased amounts of mitochondria. Mitochondria are like the power plants of a city.

(e) Endoplasmic Reticulum

The endoplasmic reticulum (ER) is a series of stacked membranes that make up the transport system of the cell. Just like a city requires roads and highways, a cell also needs a means for transporting materials from one side of the cell to the other. The ER can also produce some materials which the cell requires.

(f) Ribosomes

Ribosomes are tiny structures that are sometimes attached to the ER. They manufacture proteins that are necessary for the cell growth and reproduction. Ribosomes are like the factories of the cell.

(g) Golgi Apparatus

The Golgi apparatus is like a packaging plant in a city, where materials are sent once they have been manufactured. The Golgi apparatus builds membranes around materials which must be transported within or exported from the cell.

(h) Lysosomes

Lysosomes act like a recycling center. When the cell no longer requires material, the lysosomes take it and break it down into smaller pieces which can be reused for building other materials in the cell.

(i) Vacuoles

Vacuoles are sort of like a warehouse, as they are a storage space for materials in the cell, usually food. The vacuoles of plant cells are generally much larger than those found in animal cells because plants produce their own food and must have a large storage facility for it. (See the diagram on the next page.)

Special Plant Organelles

All animal cells have all of the above organelles; however, plant cells require two additional structures that animal cells do not, in order to carry out their functions. They require a cell wall and many tiny structures called chloroplasts.

The cell wall is a very rigid structure made of carbohydrates, cellulose and proteins.

As plant cells take in water and make food, they also expand in size. This thick, rigid wall prevents cells from bursting.

Chloroplasts are one of the most important organelles in plants because these are the structures which allow them to produce their own food. Chloroplasts contain chlorophyll, a substance which allows the cell to capture the sun's energy and transform it into a source of usable energy for the cell.

Cell Communication

Cell communication is especially important for multi-cellular plants and animals. Their cells must be capable of working together as a unit to carry out life functions. There are two types of proteins that are found on the cell membrane which allow for communication between the cells of an organism:

receptor proteins and marker proteins. In effect, cell surface receptors act as the antennae of the cell.

Receptors work by receiving chemical or electrical messages sent out by other cells. When a chemical signal is released by a cell, it binds to the receptors on other cells. This informs these cells of the situation and usually triggers the release of an enzyme. An enzyme is a molecule that speeds up a reaction in the body. For instance, when a stressful situation occurs, the body releases a hormone called epinephrine. Epinephrine binds to cells to warn them about the situation, and as a result enzymes are released to increase heart rate, blood flow to the muscles, and increase blood sugar. In this "flight or fight" response, the binding epinephrine to the liver and muscle cell receptors triggers the release of enzymes that will increase blood sugar concentration by breaking down glycogen. (See the diagram on top of the next page.)

Common Structures in Animal and Plant Cells

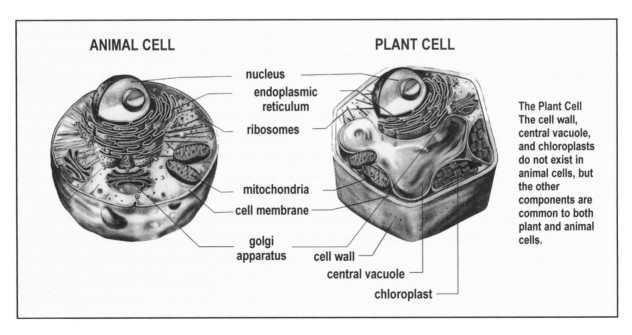

ANIMAL CELL　　　PLANT CELL

nucleus
endoplasmic reticulum
ribosomes
mitochondria
cell membrane
golgi apparatus
cell wall
central vacuole
chloroplast

The Plant Cell
The cell wall, central vacuole, and chloroplasts do not exist in animal cells, but the other components are common to both plant and animal cells.

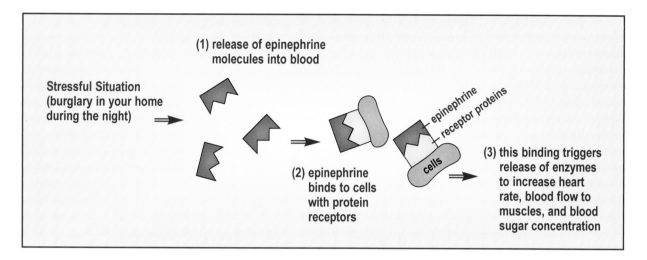

Nerve Cell and Transfer of Electrical Messages

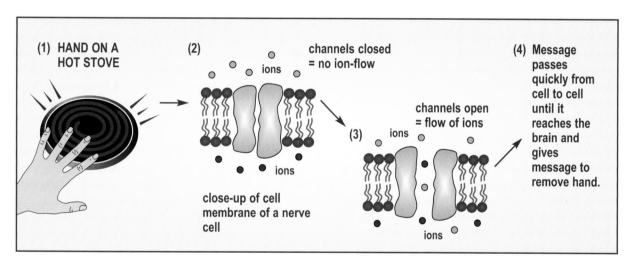

Some cells, such as nerve cells, communicate using electrical messages, instead of chemical messages. When there is an unbalanced amount of ions inside and outside of the cell, channels in the membrane that are sensitive to electricity open and allow the flow of ions. These ion channels allow currents to be carried across the membrane of nerve cells allowing messages to reach our brain so quickly. For instance, if you place your hand on a hot stovetop, in less than a second your brain has received a message from the nerve cells in your hand and has responded by activating muscles to remove your hand. (See the second diagram on this page.)

Marker proteins are also found on the cell's surface, and work in a more subtle, but very important way. Markers give cells an identity, sort of like a nametag. They separate organism's cells from foreign or invading cells. Without marker cells, the body's immune system would not be able to decide which cells to destroy and which to protect. Marker proteins also mark or indicate a cell's specialization. For instance, your heart cells have different marker proteins than your liver cells.

Surface Marker Proteins

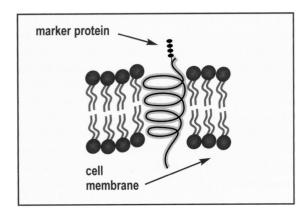

marker protein

cell membrane

Transportation of Substances

To carry out all of their crucial functions, cells are required to move all sorts of different substances in and out of the cell membrane. They have a variety of transport methods, depending on the type, the size and the amount of the molecule that must be transported.

(a) Diffusion and Osmosis

Diffusion and osmosis work under the same principle, only diffusion is the movement of solids across a membrane, while osmosis is the movement of water across a membrane. In both cases, movement of the substance occurs from an area of high concentration to an area

of low concentration. The movement continues until an equal amount of substance occurs on both sides of the membrane. This is called equilibrium. Neither process requires any energy and therefore is quite efficient for the cell.

(b) Selective Transport

Sometimes larger molecules or molecules that cannot pass through the membrane as easily as water require transportation. In this case, the cell has channels through which only certain substances can pass through. These types of channels only work in one direction, so substances cannot just pass freely in and out of the cell.

(i) Facilitated Diffusion

Facilitated diffusion is very similar to diffusion, but the molecule does not pass directly through the membrane. Instead, the molecule slides through a protein channel. This type of transport does not cost the cell any energy as the channels simply assist the diffusion process.

(ii) Active transport

In active transport, the protein channels move molecules against the regular grain of diffusion. In this way, cells can accumulate high concentrations of molecules within the cell. Because this process goes against the natural movement of materials it requires energy.

Diffusion, Osmosis Facilitated Diffusion

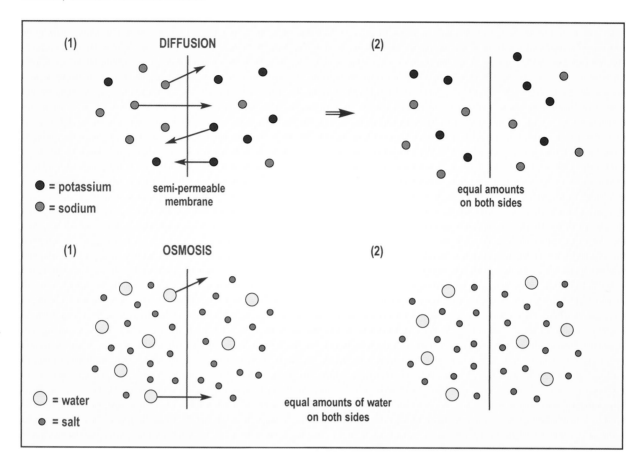

(1) **DIFFUSION** (2)

● = potassium
● = sodium

semi-permeable
membrane

equal amounts
on both sides

(1) **OSMOSIS** (2)

○ = water
● = salt

equal amounts of water
on both sides

Active Transport, Endocytosis & Exocytosis

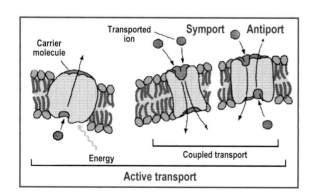

Carrier
molecule

Transported
ion

Symport   Antiport

Energy

Coupled transport

Active transport

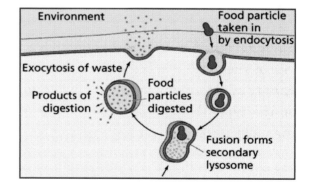

Environment

Food particle
taken in
by endocytosis

Exocytosis of waste

Products of
digestion

Food
particles
digested

Fusion forms
secondary
lysosome

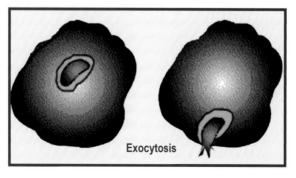

Exocytosis

(c) Endocytosis and Exocytosis

When the cell must move large molecules, it resorts to other processes called endocytosis and exocytosis. Endocytosis moves molecules into the cell by engulfing them with arm-like extensions from the membrane. Exocytosis moves molecules out of the cell by fusing with the membrane. Neither of these processes requires the molecule to actually cross the cell membrane. Both processes require energy.

Energy Use in Cells

Almost all of the cell processes that have been discussed in this lesson so far require energy. Ultimately, plants and animals get all of their energy from the sun, but solar energy is not a usable form of energy, so it must be converted.

The steps for conversion are very complex, and require numerous chemical reactions before energy can be made into a usable form for the cell. This usable form of energy is a molecule called adenosine triphosphate (ATP). The ATP molecule stores energy until the cell requires it and it can travel anywhere in the cell.

Plants capture the sun's energy and create ATP in a process called photosynthesis, while animals consume food which contains sugars from which they can form ATP through a process called cellular respiration.

The chemical formulas for photosynthesis and cellular respiration are shown below.

Photosynthesis Formula

$$6\ H_2O + 6\ CO_2 \xrightarrow[\text{(solar energy)}]{\text{+ sunlight}} 6\ O_2 + C_6H_{12}O_6$$

Cellular Respiration Formula

$$6\ O_2 + \underset{C_6H_{12}O_6}{\text{glucose}} \longrightarrow 6\ CO_2 + 6\ H_2O + \text{energy}$$

These two formulas are opposites of each other, meaning that the products of one are the reactants of the other and vice versa. This indicates a strong interdependence between these two processes.

Lesson Summary

1. Cells are extremely small because they are far more efficient that way.

2. The operation of a cell can be compared to that of a city.

3. The tiny parts of the cell are called organelles and they carry out very specific functions within the cell.

4. Cells with a nucleus are eukaryotic, while cells without a nucleus are prokaryotic.

5. Animal and plant cells have three main differences; plant cells have larger vacuoles, cell walls and chloroplasts.

6. Cells communicate using surface proteins found on the cell membranes that act as either receptors or markers.

7. Cells transport materials in many ways; diffusion, osmosis, facilitated diffusion, active transport, endocytosis and exocytosis.

8. The usable form of energy in cells is adenosine triphosphate (ATP).

9. Photosynthesis and cellular respiration are interdependent processes.

10. Photosynthesis is the process by which green plants produce sugar from carbon dioxide and water in the presence of light.

11. Cellular respiration is the process by which cells obtain energy from food.

Notes

_____

_____

_____

_____

Lesson #1 – Questions

1. Give two similarities and two differences between prokaryotic and eukaryotic cells.

_____

_____

_____

_____

_____

2. Describe how cells are able to communicate with one another using surface proteins.

_____

_____

_____

_____

_____

3. Outline the various ways that substances move in and out of the cell.

_____

_____

_____

_____

_____

4. How do photosynthesis and cellular respiration rely on one another?

_____

_____

_____

_____

_____

Lesson #2 – Cell Reproduction

Objectives:

- To describe the structure of a chromosome

- To differentiate between diploid and haploid cells

- To explain the various events of mitosis and cytokinesis

- To describe the entire cell cycle, including interphase

- To define gamete

- To summarize meiosis events and to explain how it maintains the number of chromosomes in organisms of different generations

- To explain the importance of crossing-over

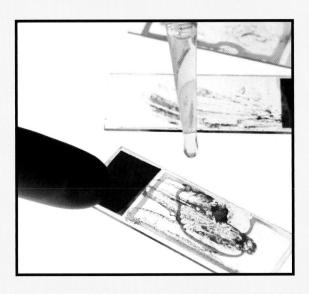

Introduction

It is difficult to talk about the study of life, biology, without discussing reproduction. Reproduction is what allows life to continue and change. Reproduction has helped people grow and develop agriculture, as well as domesticate animals to feed themselves. It has also allowed us to develop medicines, healthier foods, and also to live longer lives. At the smallest level of reproduction is cell reproduction, which has allowed you to grow and develop from the fetus that you once were. This lesson will examine the major steps involved in reproduction of the eukaryotic cell.

What are chromosomes?

From the last lesson, you learned that the nucleus of every cell contains the organism's DNA, the genetic information. The DNA, along with many other proteins, forms into structures called chromosomes. Chromosomes are simply a way for each cell to organize all of the genetic information into groups, much like you would organize your various school subjects in different binders. An organism's chromosomes contain genes for millions of different traits. Chromosomes are made of genes which are made of DNA and protein. The entire set of chromosomes is referred to as a karyotype. (See the diagrams on this page.)

Relationship Between Chromosome, Gene & DNA

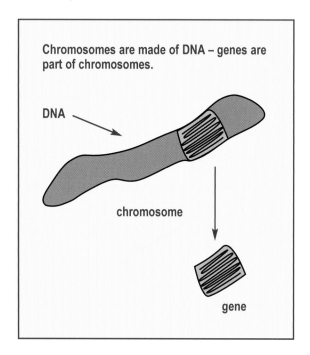

Pictures of Human Karyotype

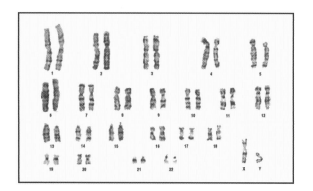

Generally, chromosomes are found in pairs. These pairs are called homologous chromosomes because they code for the same genes, but are from different parents. Humans have 23 pairs of chromosomes, for a total of 46. Every cell in a human's body, except the sex cells, has 46 chromosomes, and these are referred to as diploid cells (2n). The sex cells or gametes are the male sperm and the female egg. They contain only 23 chromosomes, half the number of chromosomes as the rest of the body's cells, and are therefore called haploid cells (n). The diploid number is the number of chromosomes, including the pairs, while the haploid number is the number of chromosomes not counting pairs.

Diploid & Haploid Cells of Humans

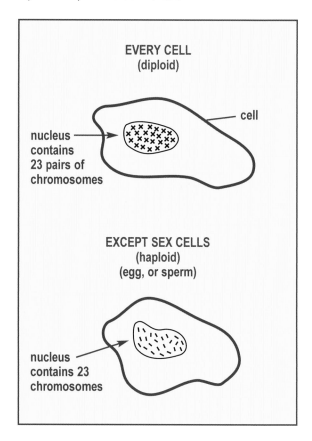

Mitosis

When the sperm and the egg unite during fertilization, they reform a cell that contains 46 chromosomes. This process is referred to as sexual reproduction. However, for this single cell to grow and develop into a multicellular organism, that initial cell must divide using a process called mitosis. Mitosis does not involve sex cells and is, for this reason, referred to as asexual reproduction. Mitosis is an extremely important part of the cell cycle.

Mitosis is the process where the nucleus of a cell divides to form two nuclei that each contains a complete and identical set of chromosomes. The goal of mitosis is to produce two cells that are genetically identical, daughter cells. In order for a cell to divide so that each new cell has the same number of chromosomes, the DNA of each cell must first be replicated. Each chromosome and its replicate are attached together by a centromere, and are called sister chromatids.

Once the DNA has been replicated mitosis can occur. Mitosis is nuclear division plus cytokinesis. In a typical animal cell, mitosis can be divided into five main stages:

(a) Prophase

During prophase, the chromosomes change from their tangled, stretched out state into visible, thick, coiled rods which can be seen with a microscope. The membrane around the nucleus begins to dissolve and structures called spindle fibres begin to appear. Spindle fibres are long, thin strands that stretch across the width of the cell from either end.

(b) Metaphase

The main step in this phase is for sister chromatids to line up along the equator of the cell. They are attached to spindle fibers and to the centromere.

(c) Anaphase

During anaphase, the members of each pair of chromatids separate from each other. As the spindle fibres contract, the individual chromatids migrate to opposite ends of the cell.

(d) Telophase

The final stage of mitosis is telophase. At this point, there are identical sets of chromosomes at either end of the cell. These chromosomes uncoil and return themselves to their long, stretched out form, while nuclear membranes form around each of the sets of chromosomes.

(e) Cytokinesis

The final step is called cytokinesis. Cytokinesis is the division of the cytoplasm and all other organelles that the cell is made of. In animal cells, the cell membrane pinches in at the middle of the cell until there are two cells. In plant cells, a plate forms in the middle of the cell and grows until separation of the two cells occurs. (See the diagram on page 90.)

Animal Cell Division

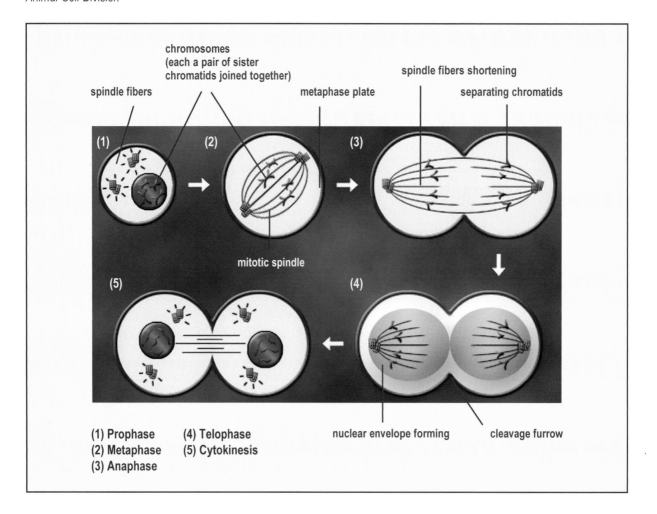

chromosomes
(each a pair of sister
chromatids joined together)

spindle fibers

metaphase plate

spindle fibers shortening

separating chromatids

(1)

(2)

(3)

mitotic spindle

(5)

(4)

nuclear envelope forming

cleavage furrow

(1) Prophase
(2) Metaphase
(3) Anaphase

(4) Telophase
(5) Cytokinesis

Plant Cell Division

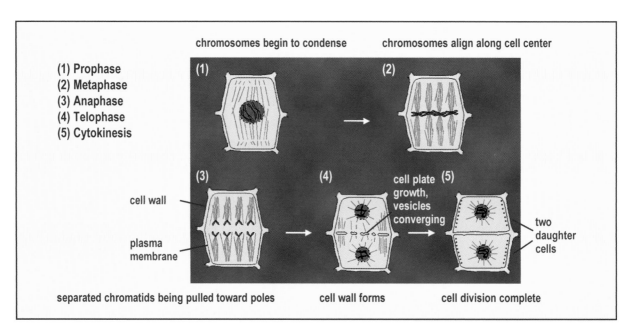

chromosomes begin to condense

chromosomes align along cell center

(1) Prophase
(2) Metaphase
(3) Anaphase
(4) Telophase
(5) Cytokinesis

(1)

(2)

(3)

(4)

cell plate (5)
growth,
vesicles
converging

cell wall

plasma
membrane

two
daughter
cells

separated chromatids being pulled toward poles

cell wall forms

cell division complete

The result of this entire process is the formation of two genetically identical cells containing the same information as the parent cell.

Although very important, mitosis is only a small part of each cell's cycle. The cell actually spends more than 90% of its time in a phase called interphase. During interphase, the chromosomes themselves are not visible under a microscope because they are in their long and tangled stage. Interphase consists of three periods. The first is a prolonged growth period (G1), followed by a synthesis period (S), and yet another growth period (G2). The S period is when the DNA is replicated for mitosis.

Pie Graph Showing Relative Lengths of each Period During Cell Cycle

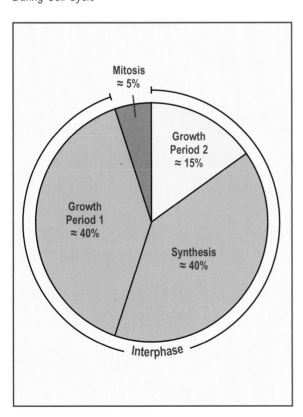

Meiosis

As mentioned earlier, the only cells in the body that are not diploid are the sex cells or gametes; the sperm (males) and the egg (females). A different process than mitosis occurs to produce gametes, it is known as meiosis. In meiosis, one diploid cell divides twice and the result is four new cells, each with a haploid number of chromosomes. These newly formed gametes are not genetically identical. Meiosis is usually broken down into two stages: meiosis I and meiosis II.

(a) Meiosis I

Like mitosis, during interphase, each chromosome is replicated. The phases of meiosis I are similar to those of mitosis; prophase I, metaphase I, anaphase I, and telophase I. One main difference between mitosis and meiosis is the stage of meiosis called crossing over. During early prophase I, as the sister chromatids are lining up on the equator of the cell, homologous chromosomes and their sister chromatids will actually switch similar portions of their chromosomes. The result is an exchange of genes between chromatids. This crossing over ensures that the resulting gametes are not identical and that variation within offspring occurs. In evolutionary terms, this is extremely important because the constant variation ensures that over time, some organisms will be more able to survive and a stronger species will develop. This process is called natural selection, or survival of the fittest.

Once crossing over takes place, the division of the cell carries forth in the same manner as mitosis. The result of this first meiotic division is two new diploid cells that are not genetically identical.

Crossing Over

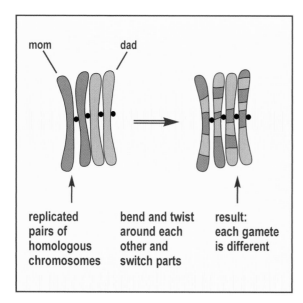

(b) Meiosis II

Before the second meiotic division, the DNA is not replicated. The second division itself occurs much like mitosis, only the result is two haploid cells, each with only half the number of chromosomes as the parent cell. This is important because it maintains the number of chromosomes within the members of one species. When gametes join during fertilization, the resulting cell is diploid, and can then undergo mitosis. Without meiosis, organisms would continue to gain more and more chromosomes each time reproduction occurred.

Meiosis in Humans

Meiosis, or gamete production, in humans occurs in both males and females. The formation of sperm in men is called spermatogenesis, and the formation of eggs in females is called oogenesis. Both are meiosis, however they have slight differences.

(a) Spermatogenesis

In males, spermatogenesis occurs in the male gonads, the testes. This process occurs from puberty on throughout most of the male's lifespan. Millions of sperm are produced each day. The process begins with the primary sperm and each time it undergoes meiosis (spermatogenesis), four non-identical sperm are produced and all are viable.

(b) Oogenesis

In females, oogenesis occurs in the female gonads, the ovaries. This process occurs during the fetal stage, when the baby is still in the mother's womb. By the time she is born, she has a supply of eggs in her own ovaries, and meiosis does not occur anymore.

Unlike spermatogenesis, oogenesis results in the formation of only one viable egg. The other three products are called polar bodies and they are not viable because there is an unequal distribution of cytoplasm between gametes.

Spermatogenesis and Oogenesis (Meiosis)

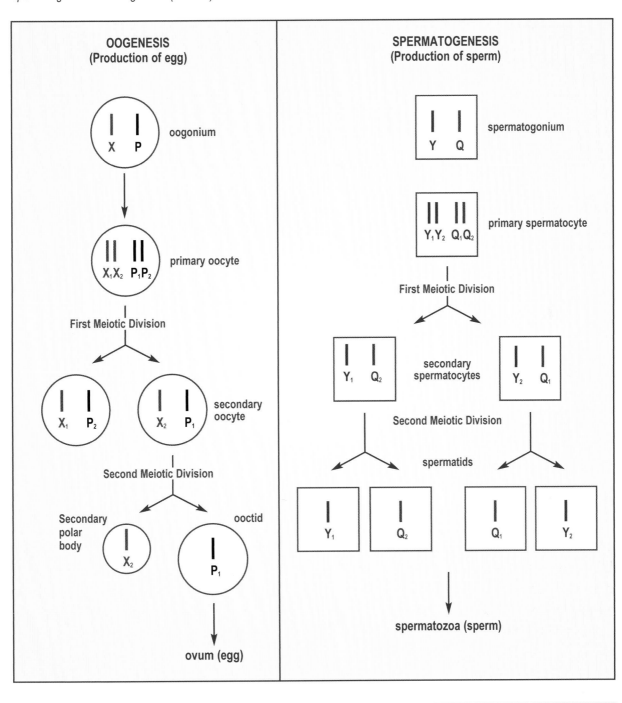

Lesson Summary

1. Chromosomes contain genes and are made of DNA.

2. Diploid cells have 2 sets of chromosomes – from mother and father. Haploid cells have only one set of chromosomes.

3. Mitosis is the reproduction and division of chromosomes of the parent cell into two new identical daughter cells. Cytokinesis is the separation of the cytoplasm.

4. Mitosis is only a small part of the entire cell cycle, which also consists of a period of growth and synthesis, called interphase.

5. A gamete is a sex cell, either a sperm or an egg, and is haploid in number.

6. Meiosis is the formation of gametes.

7. Crossing over in meiosis ensures variation among offspring, and has important evolutionary significance.

8. Spermatogenesis is meiosis in human males, while oogenesis is meiosis in human females.

Notes

_____

_____

_____

_____

_____

_____

_____

_____

_____

_____

Lesson #2 – Questions

1. Describe the difference between the chromosomes in a sperm cell compared to those of a muscle cell.

_____

_____

_____

_____

_____

_____

_____

_____

2. How does cytokinesis differ in plant and animal cells?

_____

_____

_____

_____

_____

_____

_____

_____

3. Summarize the cell cycle.

_____

_____

_____

_____

_____

_____

_____

_____

⇨

Lesson #2 – Questions (continued)

4. What function does mitosis serve?

_____

_____

_____

_____

_____

_____

_____

_____

5. Compare mitosis and meiosis.

_____

_____

_____

_____

_____

_____

_____

_____

_____

6. Describe the significance of crossing over during meiosis.

_____

_____

_____

_____

_____

_____

_____

_____

_____

Genetics

Lesson #3 – Genes and Heredity

Objectives:

- To outline Gregor Mendel's pea-plant experiments

- To describe the conclusions reached by Mendel

- To predict the results of monohybrid and dihybrid crosses using a Punnett Square

- To define the laws of Segregation and Independent Assortment as they relate to genetics

- To summarize and provide examples of other types of heredity

Introduction

There are hundreds to thousands of genes on a single chromosome, which means they are extremely small. Since this is true, how is it that as a human population we know so much about genes and heredity?

After all, the microscope was only invented in the 17th century, until then we couldn't even see a cell, much less a chromosome or a gene. Actually, much of our knowledge wasn't a result of the discovery of the microscope, it stemmed mainly from the curiosity of one scientist, Gregor Mendel. Equipped with a few pea plants, he went on to study and discover the foundation of knowledge which genetics is based on today.

Mendel and His Experiments

(a) Why Pea Plants?

Mendel chose pea plants to be his test subjects in his quest for more information about heredity. He chose pea plants as opposed to humans or

Gregor Mendal

other animals for several reasons. First, pea plants are relatively easy to grow and they are capable of producing high quantities of offspring quickly. Also, pea plants mature quite quickly, unlike most animal species. Another reason is that each pea plant contains both the male and female parts in the same flower, which makes self fertilization possible. Lastly, the physical characteristics of pea plants are not as varied as many other animal species. For instance, pea plant flowers only have two possible colors – purple or white. Their seeds are either green or yellow, and round or wrinkled, and their height is either short or tall. Choosing a species with simple characteristics was important for Mendel so that he could easily follow these traits through the generations.

(b) The Basic Experiment

Mendel's basic experiment was set up as follows:

1. He created a generation of pure breeding plants to be the parents. He did this by self-fertilizing plants, from generation to generation, until the only type of offspring was identical to the parent. This pure-breeding set of plants was called the P generation, for parents. Some of the plants were pure-breeding for purple flowers, while others were pure-breeding for white flowers.

2. He crossed two different plants from the P generation, a white and a purple. The offspring from these P x P crosses were named the first filial generation, or F1. The result of every cross of the P generation resulted in all purple-flowered plants.

3. He then crossed two of the plants from the F1 generation. The offspring from these F1 x F1 crosses were named the second filial generation, or F2. The result of these crosses produced offspring in the ratio of 3:1 purple to white.

Different Possibilities of Characteristics in Pea Plants

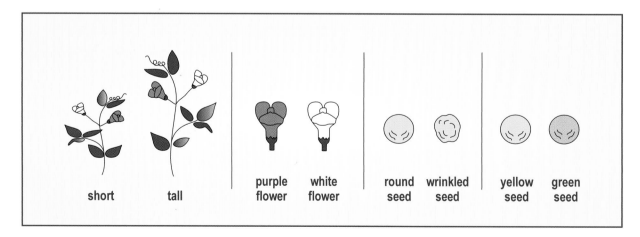

| short | tall | purple flower | white flower | round seed | wrinkled seed | yellow seed | green seed |

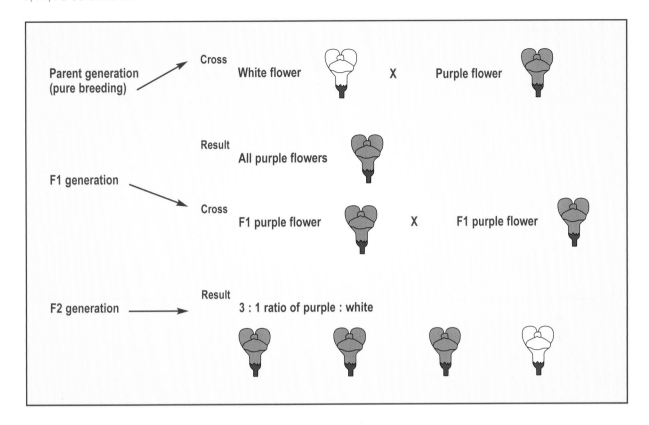

(c) Mendel's Conclusions

Mendel made some brilliant conclusions based on these results, all of which still hold true today. The most basic of conclusions was that parents pass on information about physical traits to their offspring. He referred to these traits as factors. For example, all of the F1 must have received a purple factor from the parent because they all had purple flowers.

Today, we know that it is genes that are passed on from parent to offspring, not factors. For instance, the gene for flower color has two possibilities; purple and white, and these possibilities are called alleles.

The next conclusion was that each offspring receives only one allele from each parent, although the parents have two. In the case of his basic experiment, there arose a problem with this idea. If a purple pure-breeding plant passes on a purple allele and a white pure-breeding plant passes on a white allele, how is it that none of the offspring have white flowers? Mendel hypothesized that some alleles are expressed in the physical traits of the plants, and they are called dominant alleles, while others are masked, and they are called recessive alleles. In the case of the pea plants, although all of the F1 plants carry both the white and purple factors, the white was masked and the purple was expressed. Therefore, purple flowers are dominant, and white flowers are recessive in pea plants.

Pea Plant Traits / Human Traits

Pea Plant Trait	Dominant	Recessive
Flower Color	Purple (W)	White (w)
Seed Color	Yellow (Y)	Green (y)
Seed Texture	Round (R)	Wrinkled (r)
Plant Height	Tall (T)	Short (t)

Human Trait	Dominant	Recessive
Type of Thumb	Straight	Hitchhikers Thumb
Hairline	Straight	Widow's Peak
Earlobes	Not Attached (Free)	Attached
Tongue Rolling	Tongue Roller	Non Tongue Roller

Today, the combinations of the alleles are known as the genotype, while the physical traits that are expressed in the individual are the phenotype. Genotype determines phenotype. Individuals like the pea plants in the P generation are called homozygous because they carry two purple alleles or two white alleles, while individuals from the F1 generation are called heterozygous because they carry one of each allele.

Difference Between Phenotype & Genotype

(1) Genotype	Phenotype
WW	Purple Flower
Ww	Purple Flower
ww	White Flower

(2) Genotype	Phenotype
YyRr	Yellow, Round Seed
YYrr	Yellow, Wrinkled Seed
yyRR	Green, Round Seed

The Law of Segregation (Mendel's First Law)

The law of segregation states that the members of each pair of alleles separate when gametes are formed. A gamete will receive only one allele or the other. To put this in context, during meiosis, each of the gametes that are formed contains only half of the number of chromosomes, and half the number of alleles. For example, a plant from the F1 generation has a 50% chance of passing on the purple allele, and a 50% chance of passing on the white allele. (See the diagram on the next page.)

Law of Segregation (formation of gametes)

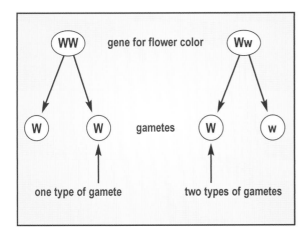

Law of Independent Assortment
(formation of gametes with more than one trait)

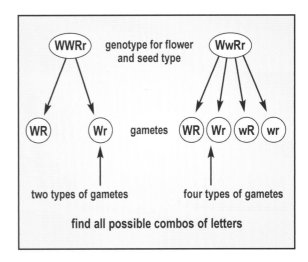

The Law of Independent Assortment (Mendel's Second Law)

Next Mendel wondered if traits could be transmitted to offspring as units. To test this question, he crossed plants with contrasting forms of two traits, a dihybrid cross, such as plants that had round, yellow seeds with plants that had wrinkled, green seeds. The F1 generation all had seeds that were round and yellow (dominant traits), however the F2 generation exhibited a variety of phenotypes. This is the basis for the law of independent assortment which states that two or more pairs of alleles segregate independently of one another during meiosis. Simply stated, this means that the inheritance for one trait does not affect the inheritance of another trait. For example, whether a plant is short or tall does not affect whether its seeds are round or wrinkled.

Punnett Squares

In order to better visualize these crosses, a form of letter notation has been designated to represent the recessive and dominant alleles, and a mathematical tool called a Punnett Square is also employed.

The dominant allele of a trait is always represented using an upper case letter, while the recessive trait is represented by using the corresponding lower case letter. For example, the recessive white allele is represented by the letter "w", while the dominant allele for purple flowers is represented using the letter "W". A plant that is homozygous for the purple flower allele is "WW", a plant that is homozygous for the white flower allele is "ww", and the heterozygous plant is "Ww".

The Punnett Square is simply a tool used for predicting the outcomes of various crosses. On one side of the square, all of

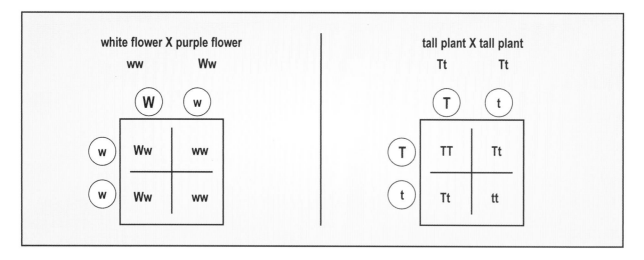

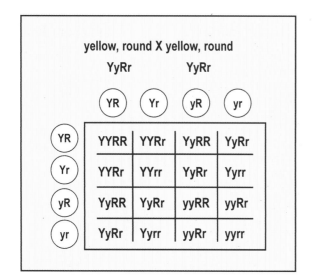

the possible gametes are listed for one parent, and on the top of the square, all of the possible gametes are listed for the other parent. The results of the combination of each gamete are filled in the squares within the center of the square. (See above.)

The Punnett Square is also useful in predicting outcomes for dihybrid crosses, which are crosses where you want to predict the outcome of two traits.

Two Dihybrid Crosses and Punnett Squares

Other Types of Heredity

Mendel's dominant and recessive alleles explain many traits, but not all. It certainly cannot explain why there are so many varieties in eye or skin color, or why a tall and a short parent can produce a child with medium height, or why a red and a white flower can be crossed to make a pink one. That is because there are many different types of heredity. In this lesson we will explore four types: incomplete dominance, co-dominance and multiple alleles.

(a) Incomplete Dominance

In incomplete dominance, neither allele is dominant therefore the heterozygous individuals express a blend of the two possible phenotypes. Since there is no dominant trait, lower case letters are used to represent each allele.

This type of heredity is exhibited in Andalusian fowl. Some individuals have black feathers "bb", some have white feathers "ww", and some exhibit grey feathers, a blend of the other two, "bw". Another example occurs in Four O'clock flowers, where the homozygotes are red "rr" and white "ww", while the heterozygote is pink "rw".

There are two steps to *recognize* when you are dealing with a question involving incomplete dominance:

1. Notice that the offspring is showing a 3rd phenotype. The parents each have one, and the offspring are different from the parents.

2. Notice that the trait in the offspring is a blend (mixing) of the parental traits.

Four O'Clock Flowers   *Andalusian Fowl*
Heterozygous is Pink   *Heterozygous is Grey*

Co-dominance / Horse —› Coat is Roan

(b) Co-dominance

Co-dominance is a type of heredity where there is evidence of both traits being expressed in the same individual. Since both traits are dominant, upper case letters are used to represent each allele. For instance, skin color in frogs is co-dominant. Some frogs are green "GG", some are brown "BB", and some are green with brown spots "GB". Another example occurs in the coats of some cattle. Some have red coats "RR", some have white coats "WW", while others have coats with red and white hairs (roan) "RW".

(c) Multiple Alleles

In the other types of heredity so far, each gene was considered to have only two possible alleles. However, some genes exist for which there are more than two alleles. Even though multiple alleles exist, individuals may still only possess two of them, one from each parent. The result is many different possible combinations of alleles, and phenotypes. The most common example of multiple allele heredity is human blood type. The alleles of this gene are designated as follows: I^A codes for A blood type, I^B codes for B blood type and i codes for type O blood. From the notation for each, you can see that types A and B are dominant over type O, however, they are co-dominant with one another. This results in the following genotypes and phenotypes.

Genotypes and Phenotypes for Human Blood Groups

Genotype	Phenotype
ii	Blood type O
$I^A I^A$, $I^A i$	Blood type A
$I^B I^B$, $I^B i$	Blood type B
$I^A I^B$	Blood type AB

Lesson Summary

1. Gregor Mendel introduced the world to genetics through his experiments with pea plants. He used pea plants because they reproduce and mature quickly and they have relatively simple physical traits.

2. He crossed pure-breeding purple flowered plants with pure-breeding white flowered plants and all of the F1 offspring were purple-flowered plants, while the F2 offspring exhibited both traits.

3. Mendel concluded that some alleles are dominant over others. The dominant gene is expressed in the phenotype of an individual and the recessive gene is masked.

4. Mendel's Laws of Segregation states that when gametes are formed, the alleles separate so that only one allele for each gene is present in the gametes.

5. Mendal's Law of Independent Assortment states that each gene is an independent unit that is inherited on its own.

6. There are other types of heredity: incomplete dominance, co-dominance, and multiple alleles.

Notes

_____

_____

_____

_____

_____

_____

_____

_____

_____

_____

_____

Lesson #3 – Questions

1. In humans, the gene T for tongue-rolling is dominant over the gene t for non-rolling. Predict the likelihood that the offspring would be able to roll their tongues if the mother is a homozygous tongue-roller and the father is a non-roller.

_____

_____

_____

_____

_____

_____

_____

2. Predict the genotypes of F1 using a Punnett square. A pure-breeding tall pea plant with yellow seeds (TTYY) is crossed with a heterozygote for both genes (TtYy).

_____

_____

_____

_____

_____

_____

_____

_____

3. Cattle show co-dominant heredity in coat color, where the homozygotes have either red or white coats and the heterozygote has both colors in a roan colored coat. Predict the phenotypes of the offspring if a white and a roan are crossed.

_____

_____

_____

_____

_____

_____

_____

Lesson #3 – Questions (continued)

4. A certain type of snapdragon has homozygotes that are white and red, but the heterozygote is pink. What type of heredity is this? What are the genotypes of the parents if all of the F1 generation are pink?

_____

_____

_____

_____

_____

_____

_____

5. Use a Punnett square to determine the possible blood types for the offspring of parents with type AB and type B blood. Consider all possibilities.

Notes

_____

_____

_____

_____

_____

_____

_____

Lesson #4 – Biotechnology

Objectives:

• To understand the basic structure of DNA

• To define the concept of biotechnology

• To explain the basic tools of biotechnology and how they relate, using an example

• To provide examples of how biotechnology and genetic engineering are being used in the field of agriculture

• To define the term clone in a biological context

• To outline how the first cloned organism arose (Dolly)

• To identify some of the impacts, positive and negative, that human cloning presents

Introduction

Although Gregor Mendel is nicknamed the father of genetics, since his time there have been several major advances in our understanding and use of the science of genetics. In 1997, the first ever cloned organism was born to a surrogate mother, and since then others have followed. It seems the possibility of human cloning is just around the corner. In 2000, the first draft of the human genome was published, demonstrating our vast knowledge of how human genes operate. This has led to a rapid increase in the quickness with which solutions to medical problems are being found. A stroll through the produce section in the grocery store reveals many new genetically modified *vegetables such as broco-flower, a genetic combination of broccoli and cauliflower. Furthermore, using DNA as evidence in courtrooms across the world has become the norm. Biotechnology is behind the success of many of these projects and advances. In this lesson, we will explore DNA itself, as well as some of the tools used in biotechnology and some of its impacts, positive and negative.*

The Structure of DNA

Every deoxyribonucleic acid (DNA) molecule is made of thousands of nucleotides, strung together to form long chains. Each nucleotide consists of three parts; a sugar called deoxyribose, a

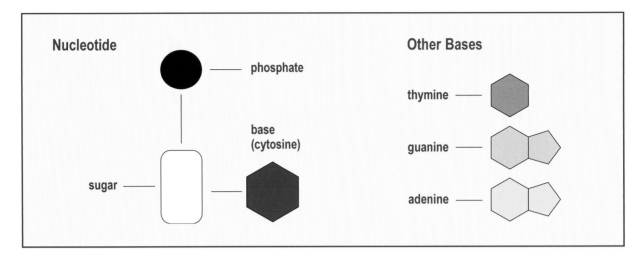

phosphate group and a nitrogenous base. The sugar and phosphate groups are the same in every nucleotide, but the bases change. There are four possible bases. The two larger bases are adenine (A) and guanine (G), while the two smaller bases are cytosine (C) and thymine (T).

Each base has a complement base, with which it forms a hydrogen bond. Adenine and thymine bond together to form a complementary base pair while cytosine and guanine bond together to form a different complementary base pair. When these base pairs are formed, what results is a double helix structure, a sort of twisted ladder, where the base pairs are on the inside facing one another and the

Double Helix Structure of DNA

sugar and phosphate groups are on the outside. It was scientists James Watson and Francis Crick who were awarded the Nobel Prize in 1962 for their work on this model of DNA.

This model readily explains how it is possible for DNA to replicate itself during cell reproduction. The two strands in each DNA molecule are complementary, which means that the order of the bases on one of the strands determines the order on the other one. For instance, if the order is CGGAT on the first strand, the only possible combination on the other strand must be GCCTA. If the DNA molecule is separated, then each strand would code for the missing strand, therefore it would be possible to replicate each strand.

It is also important to understand that each DNA molecule and its different base sequences is a set of instructions to make proteins. Since DNA cannot leave the nucleus, a copy that can leave the nucleus must first be made. Transcription is the process where a copy of the DNA is made and the product is a single strand of ribonucleic

DNA Replication

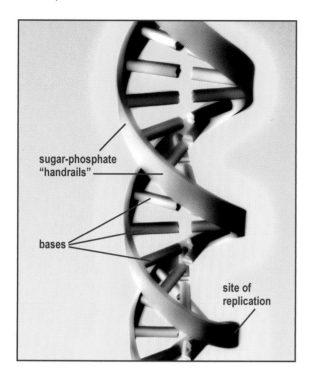

sugar-phosphate "handrails"

bases

site of replication

that geneticists use in biotechnology in order to better understand this new and exciting field of science.

Diagram of DNA Replication

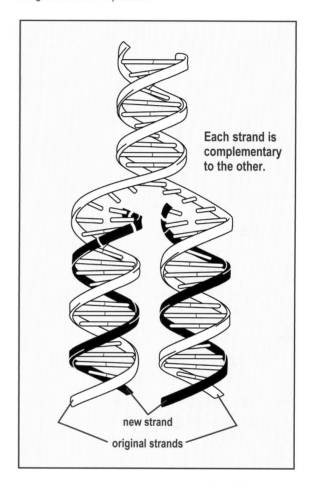

Each strand is complementary to the other.

new strand

original strands

acid (RNA). The RNA can travel out of the nucleus into the cell where it is used to make proteins that the cell requires. Translation is the process where the cell ribosomes decode the sequence of bases to make proteins. A series of three bases is called a codon because it codes for a particular amino acid. Long chains of amino acids are what make up proteins. Four tiny bases can code for thousands of proteins because there are about 20 amino acids which can each form thousands of sequences.

Two Main Tools in Biotechnology

Biotechnology uses the knowledge we have about living organisms and their genetic make-ups to create and improve products, and also to facilitate many biological processes. It is important to know about the basic tools

Diagram of DNA Transcription and Translation

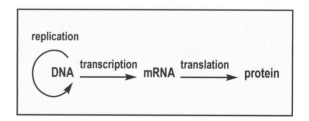

replication

DNA →transcription→ mRNA →translation→ protein

We will examine how biotechnology is being used today to help diabetic patients lead better lives. Diabetes is a disease that renders the body unable to control the sugar levels in blood and tissues. This occurs largely because the body fails to produce adequate quantities of insulin, a hormone that assists with this process. In order to produce insulin in the laboratory, scientists have isolated the gene for insulin production in healthy people, and have inserted it into bacterial cells that can produce large quantities of insulin for diabetic patients. The big questions are: How did they isolate this gene? How did they manage to get it into bacterial cells and how do the bacteria actually begin producing insulin?

(a) Restriction Enzymes

Restriction enzymes are what allow the desired genes to be separated from all of the other genes, for example the insulin production gene in healthy people. They work by cutting DNA at very specific points in their base sequences, much like a pair of scissors might. Each restriction enzyme has a certain sequence, called a recognition sequence, which it cuts when found. For instance, maybe the recognition sequence is AATGCA, and the cut is made between the two A's. This enzyme will make identical cuts on both strands of the DNA. When another molecule of the same restriction enzyme makes the same cuts further down a DNA molecule, the result is a fragment or piece of the original. A particular segment of DNA, a gene, has been isolated from the larger chain.

Diagram of Restriction Enzymes Cutting a Recognition Sequence, and the New DNA Fragment with "Sticky Ends"

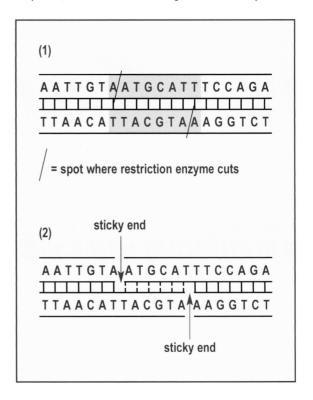

"Sticky End" can attract Complementary Strand

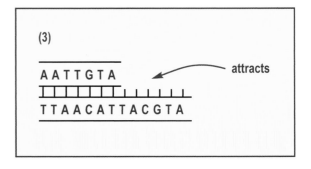

Note that with this particular restriction enzyme, each end of the fragment has a strand that protrudes. These ends are called "sticky ends" because they are able to attract their complementary base pairs under the proper conditions. In our example, the protruding end sequence AGTC is capable of attracting complementary bases TCAG from any piece of DNA.

There are many different restriction enzymes, each having their own recognition sequences, and each useful in isolating different genes.

(b) Plasmids

Once a gene is isolated, plasmids act as the delivery vehicle into the bacterial cell, where the gene can be mass produced. Plasmids are rings of bacterial DNA that lie outside of the single chromosome in a bacterial cell. They make excellent vehicles for DNA because they are able to move freely in and out of bacterial cells, incorporating the new gene into the DNA production of the cell.

Diagram of a Plasmid Ring

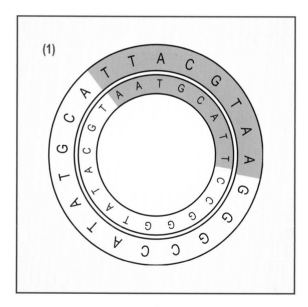

The same restriction enzyme is then applied to the plasmid, and when a cut is made, it opens the circular plasmid, creating a "sticky end" at each opening. These "sticky ends" have complementary base sequences to the fragment, allowing the DNA fragment, or isolated gene, to

become part of the plasmid ring. The new plasmid ring is called recombinant DNA because the new gene has been combined with the plasmid DNA to form a base sequence that does not exist in nature.

DNA Fragment Joining with Plasmid Ring that Has Been Cut

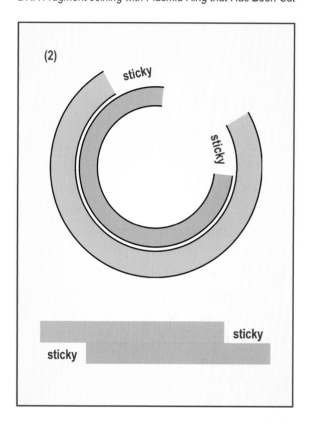

Once inside the bacterial cell, the desired human gene, the insulin production gene, is replicated and the proteins necessary to build insulin are formed. This same process used to make insulin for diabetic patients, is also used to make many other proteins.

Genetic Engineering in Agriculture

Using similar methods to those outlined above, researchers have been able to successfully isolate and insert designer genes in plants, thus eliminating the undesirable gene. The only difference is that the plasmids used are not always bacterial.

For example, the development of crops that are resistant to herbicides has been a huge improvement to farmers. The gene that causes resistance to herbicides has been inserted into crops, so that farmers can simply spray their crops with a herbicide, and all undesired plants and weeds will die, while the herbicide resistant crop will remain. Along the same lines, researchers have success-fully inserted the gene for resistance to insects into some plants, so that insects that attempt to eat the plant die immediately. This has a very positive outcome for farmers because they do not lose crops to insects, and this method is not harmful to the environment like most  insecticides. Another example which has not been successful yet, but is underway is the insertion of the nitrogen-fixing gene from some plants into others which do not possess the gene. All plants require nitrogen, but are not able to get it into a useable form without the assistance of bacteria or fertilizers. By placing this gene into crops like wheat, corn, and rice, the hope is that farmers' expenses will be reduced greatly by eliminating the need to purchase expensive nitrogen-rich fertilizers for their crops. These are just a few of the ways that biotechnology and genetic engineering are making positive changes to the field of agriculture.

Cloning

To clone something is to "make an exact copy of". Cloning is a relatively new branch of genetics, and is surrounded by controversy. Whether it is cloning of a single gene, as in the example just described, or an organ, or an entire organism, cloning has its pros and cons. We have examined how it is 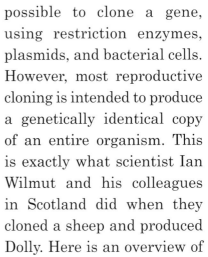 possible to clone a gene, using restriction enzymes, plasmids, and bacterial cells. However, most reproductive cloning is intended to produce a genetically identical copy of an entire organism. This is exactly what scientist Ian Wilmut and his colleagues in Scotland did when they cloned a sheep and produced Dolly. Here is an overview of the basic steps that were taken to clone this organism.

1. The DNA of a sheep was donated in the form of a few udder cells.

2. An egg cell of a second sheep was also donated, and the nucleus containing the DNA of this egg was removed.

3. The DNA from the first donor was fused with the empty egg from the second donor, using a powerful jolt of electricity.

4. The DNA in the egg is reprogrammed, by the organelles of the egg cell, to act like an embryo.

5. This egg cell is implanted in the uterus of a third sheep, a surrogate mother.

6. The resulting offspring is an exact clone of the sheep that donated the DNA.

Steps of the Creation of Dolly

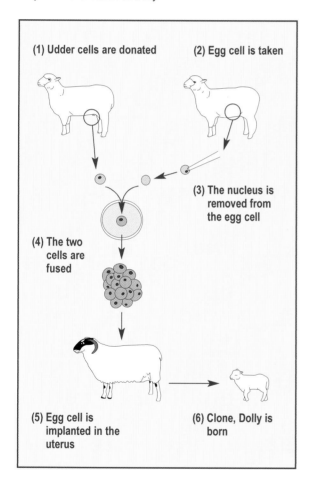

(1) Udder cells are donated

(2) Egg cell is taken

(3) The nucleus is removed from the egg cell

(4) The two cells are fused

(5) Egg cell is implanted in the uterus

(6) Clone, Dolly is born

At first glance, this cloning possibility doesn't seem like such a bad idea. Strong, healthy animals and plants, in agricultural situations, could easily be cloned, and weaker ones eliminated. However, whenever the possibility of human cloning is presented, there are many concerns.

Looking at the positive side of human cloning first, women who have miscarriages would be able to take DNA from the miscarried fetus and attempt the pregnancy again, perhaps in a surrogate mother, by cloning the fetus. Couples who are infertile would be able to have children that possess at least one of their sets of genes. Since, genes are not the only factors controlling the traits of organisms; a human clone would not be exactly the same as the original person. The environment plays a great role in the expression of physical and other traits, in fact human clones would probably be less alike than identical twins, because they would not be raised in the same environment.

However, there are definitely some negative impacts of human cloning. First of all, hundreds of attempts may have to be made before a viable embryo is actually produced, and often animals that are cloned have physical defects and are abnormally large. Given these animal results, one might wonder if it would be ethical to even try to clone a human. From a theological perspective, many would argue that it is unethical to interfere with nature's ways.

Whatever side you take, it is important to see both sides of the argument, and also to realize that this possibility is real, in fact it is just around the corner.

Lesson Summary

1. The basic structure of DNA consists of two chains of nucleotides, twisted into a double-helix shape. Each nucleotide is made up of a sugar, a phosphate and a base.

2. The four bases are adenine (A), guanine (G), thymine (T) and cytosine (C). Adenine and thymine are complementary bases, while cytosine and guanine are complementary.

3. Transcription is the process where DNA is copied into an RNA form which can leave the nucleus of the cell. Translation is the process where ribosomes decode the RNA base sequence to make proteins for the cell.

4. Biotechnology uses tools like restriction enzymes, plasmids and bacteria in order to create and improve on products, or to facilitate processes.

5. Restriction enzymes are like scissors that cut DNA into fragments, so that certain genes can be isolated. Plasmids are the DNA delivery vehicles that are used to transport the desired gene into the organism.

6. Genetic engineering and biotechnology have greatly improved agricultural practices by producing crops that are resistant to herbicides and insecticides.

7. Cloning is defined as "making an exact copy of" something.

8. The first ever cloned organism was a sheep named Dolly. The DNA and egg of different donors were used to create a new embryo which was implanted into a surrogate mother's uterus, and the resulting offspring was an exact copy of the sheep donor.

9. Human cloning is a very real possibility in the near future. There are several positive and negative impacts of human cloning.

Lesson #4 – Questions

1. Describe the structure of DNA.

_____

_____

_____

_____

2. What is the purpose of translation?

_____

_____

_____

3. Outline the function of restriction enzymes in biotechnology.

_____

_____

_____

4. Why are plasmids used as the DNA delivery vehicle in genetic engineering?

_____

_____

_____

5. Summarize the events leading up to the cloning of the first organism.

_____

_____

_____

_____

_____

_____

Classification of Living Organisms

Lesson #5 – Classification of Living Organisms

Objectives:

- To name the characteristics of living organisms

- To understand the need for a universal classification system

- To explain the scientific system for naming organisms

- To describe the hierarchical classification of organisms

- To distinguish between methods of classification used by taxonomists

- To interpret how evolution plays a role in the classification of organisms

- To define the term species

- To list major properties of each of the six kingdoms of living organisms

Introduction

Before classifying living organisms, it only makes sense to ensure that we have a solid definition about what it actually means to be alive. It is likely that you already have a fairly good idea about what living is, but in this section we will examine this concept more closely. We will also study the importance of classification and how it is helping scientists slowly piece together the puzzle of our past. We will learn that there are six major categories, called kingdoms in which living organisms can be classified.

Characteristics of Living Organisms

If you encounter something on a walk in the park and you are not sure if it is alive or not, what would you look for in order to make your decision? First, you might determine if it is capable of moving. You might also check to see if it responds to the poke or prod of a stick, and maybe you would even keep it for a while to determine if it was growing or changing, or if it would eventually die. Most living organisms do all of these things, however, there is no guarantee that something is alive if it possesses one of these qualities. For instance, a kite will fly and move about in the wind like a bird, however it is not alive. A mushroom does not really respond to a poke of a stick, yet it is considered living. A television will stop working, or 'die', but it is not alive. In order to clarify a proper definition for living, we must establish some characteristics that apply to all organisms.

The following are the primary six characteristics used in determining if an organism is alive or not.

1. **Metabolism** – all living things have the ability to take energy from the environment, use it, and change it from one form to another. They are highly specialized at energy conversion.

2. **Homeostasis** – all living things are able to maintain a very stable internal environment. As an example, living things maintain relatively constant concentrations of oxygen and carbon dioxide in their blood.

3. **Reproduction** – all living things can produce organisms that are genetically similar or even identical to themselves.

4. **Inheritance** – all living things have the ability to pass on characteristics from parent to offspring generation after generation.

5. **Cellular Make-Up** – all living things are made up of cells.

6. **Response** – all living things respond to changes in the environment (stimuli). For example, web-building spiders are sensitive to the slightest vibrations of their web. They can distinguish between vibrations caused by the wind and those caused by an intruder.

Scientific System for Naming Organisms

Similar to the metric system or the elements of the periodic table, a universal method of naming organisms was required because scientists all over the world were working at classifying organisms in various languages. Latin was chosen to be the universal language used by scientists in classification of organisms, which may seem absurd because Latin is no longer a spoken language. However, it is really not that surprising because Latin was the language used most commonly among scholars and academics in the past. Because many scientific names had already been chosen in Latin, it made sense to continue using this language, rather than switch it to a language such as French or English.

Leopard

Lion

Binomial Nomenclature System

Each specific living organism is given a scientific name that is composed of two words. The first word represents the genus of the organism. A genus name simply indicates a grouping for organisms that share major characteristics. The second word represents the species of the organism. A species name indicates one particular type of organism within the specified genus. For example, the scientific name for leopard is *Panthera pardus*, where *Panthera* is the genus name and *pardus* is the species name. The lion is part of the same genus as the leopard but has a different species name, *Panthera leo*.

In terms of the rules for making up scientific names, the scientific name of an organism can only be used once. However, it is common for different organisms to share either the first or second word of their scientific name. For instance, any two organisms which are part of the same genus will share the first word of their name, and as you might suspect, this happens quite often. For instance, the golden jackal (*Canis aureus*), the gray wolf (*Canis lupus*), the red wolf (*Canis rufus*), the coyote (*Canis latrans*), and the dog (*Canis familiaris*) are all from the genus Canis. Often the species name will describe a physical characteristic or area in which it is found.

Jackal

Wolf

Coyote

Dog

Less commonly, it is also possible for two organisms or more, to share the species name, but be part of different genera (plural for genus). This is true in the case of the green anole lizard, *Anolis carolinensis*, and the chickadee, *Parus carolinensis*. They are both found in both North and South Carolina.

Lizard

Chickadee

There are also some rules that apply to the scientific name notation. The genus name is always capitalized, while the species name is written in lower-case letters, but both names are always italicized or underlined. Also, it is common practice to shorten the genus name to just the first letter, once introduced into the writing. Since I have already referred to *Canis lupus* in writing, I could simply write it as *C. lupus*.

Taxonomy

Taxonomy is the science of classifying living organisms, and is therefore one of the many branches of biology. The system of classification that scientists use is one of hierarchy, which simply means that each organism is part of a larger group, which is part of an even larger group. There are seven levels in our present system. In order from largest to smallest, they are Kingdom, Phylum, Class, Order, Family, Genus, and Species. This means that a species is part of a genus, and every member of the genus is part of a larger group, the family, and every member of the family is part of a larger group still, the order, and so on. (See the diagram below.)

Upon examination of the classification of the lion, it is evident that the more levels that are shared between two species, the more traits they have in common and hence the more closely related they are.

The lion shares three levels with humans, whereas it shares six levels with the jaguar. The lion and the jaguar can be easily compared; they both have similar size, bones, fur, teeth, speed, eating habits, and so on. In this particular case, the lion and the jaguar are very closely related. In fact, their similarities are strong evidence that a genetic change in this species has occurred over time. This is called evolution. Because the lion and the jaguar share many traits means that they also shared a common ancestor not long ago.

However, sharing similarities does not always mean a close relationship. For instance, a shark and a dolphin have many similar characteristics, but they actually have far more differences than similarities. The fact that both have sleek bodies, flat tails and fins is not a result of a common ancestor, but rather the result of convergent evolution. Convergent evolution means that two species have

Classification

Kingdom	Animalia	L	J	H	F	S	B	Sn	G
Phylum	Chordata	L	J	H	F	S	B		G
Class	Mammalia	L	J	H			B		G
Order	Primates			H					G
Genus	Homo			H					
Species	Sapiens			H					

Lion = L	Snake =S	Human = H	Fish = F
Jaguar = J	Bear = B	Snail = Sn	Gorilla = G

developed similar structures, likely as a result of having similar habitats. These are called analogous structures because they evolved independently, not from a common ancestor. These three characteristics of both the shark and the dolphin have been selected over the years in a process called natural selection. Natural selection is a process where organisms that are best equipped for their surroundings are most likely to survive and reproduce. It is evident that convergent evolution could create problems for scientists during their quest for classification of all living organisms, and so taxonomy is not a science of facts and most hypotheses are often debated at length before being proven or disproven.

In recent years, technology has greatly influenced the ability of taxonomists to make classification decisions about different organisms much more quickly than in the past. The use of DNA sequencing techniques is often used to decide about the degree of similarity between two or more organisms. The more sequences the DNA of each organism have in common, the more closely they are related, and the more recently they shared a common ancestor.

Types of Taxonomy

There are two branches of taxonomy; cladistics and phenetics. Cladistics uses shared derived characteristics to determine the order of branching events from the common ancestor. It is concerned only with evolutionary relationships, not classification. The disadvantage to this method is that the differences between organisms are not revealed because only similarities are compared. These relationships are represented in a diagram that resembles a tree, called a cladogram.

Cladogram for a Selected Group of Mammalian Carnivores

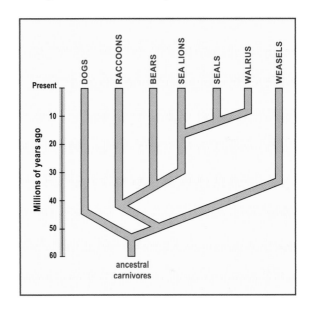

The second branch of taxonomy is called phenetics and considers as many similar characteristics as possible to look for an overall degree of similarity between two organisms. Phenetics does not observe evolutionary relationships; it simply groups organisms so that naming can take place more easily.

What is it that ultimately defines a species? We know that it is the last level of classification, however, why does the classification stop there? The more traditional definition recognizes a species as being able to interbreed to produce fertile offspring. Let us use our previous example of the lion and the jaguar. Although they are part of the same genus *(Panthera)*, when bred, the resulting hybrid is not fertile. Some exceptions do occur, for instance dogs, wolves and coyotes can interbreed to produce fertile offspring, yet they are all considered separate species. Also, this definition does not consistently apply in the plant kingdom because most hybrids are fertile. In general terms, a species is a unique organism that possesses at least one inherited trait not found in any other similar organism.

The Six Kingdoms of Living Organisms

All living organisms are categorized in one of the six kingdoms; Archaebacteria, Eubacteria, Protista, Fungi, Plantae or Animalia.

(a) Archaebacteria and Eubacteria

All bacteria fall into either one of these categories. Bacteria are the oldest form of organism; single-cells with no nucleus (prokaryotes). Their organelles are not surrounded by membranes and their genetic material is not organized in chromosomes as in animal cells. They range in the way they obtain their nutrients, some are heterotrophs (must obtain nutrients from outside source) while others are autotrophs (can make their own food). The main difference between the kingdoms is the type of habitat in which the bacteria live. Archaebacteria live in extreme environments, ranging from abnormal temperatures, salt concentrations or oxygen deprived environments. There are only about 100 different species found in this kingdom, the least of all

Diagrams of Two Hybrids – One Plant & One Animal

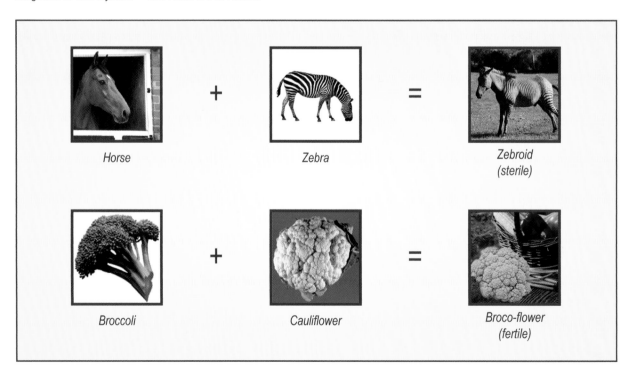

Horse   +   Zebra   =   Zebroid (sterile)

Broccoli   +   Cauliflower   =   Broco-flower (fertile)

kingdoms. Eubacteria, on the other hand, live in more common environments such as food, skin, or water.

(b) Protista

The Protista kingdom is the most diverse kingdom. Organisms which fall into this category are unicellular, except for algae organisms, and differ from bacteria in that their cells have nuclei (eukaryotes) and their organelles are organized by membranes. Most Protista have chloroplasts which mean that they can produce their own food with the help of sunlight.

(c) Fungi

Like Protista, the organisms in the Fungi kingdom are eukaryotic, but they are more complex because they are multi-cellular. Fungi are heterotrophs, and unlike plants they do not have roots or leaves, they are composed of thin, heterotrophic filaments which embed themselves in the soil to absorb nutrients. The most common type of fungi are mushrooms and yeasts.

(d) Plantae

Organisms that are part of the Plantae kingdom are multi-cellular eukaryotes and photosynthetic, which means they can make their own food. Some common examples of plants are trees, mosses and ferns.

(e) Animalia

Like plants, organisms of the Animalia kingdom are also multi-cellular eukaryotes, however they are different in that animals do not produce their own food, they ingest it. The primary method of reproduction is sexual, and animals can live both on land and in water. Humans are part of this kingdom, along with more than one million other species. Animalia is the largest kingdom of all.

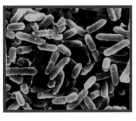
Bacteria

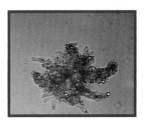
Protista

Fungi

Plantæ

Animalia

Lesson Summary

1. The six main characteristics defining living organisms are: metabolism, homeostasis, reproduction, inheritance, cellular make-up and response.

2. The scientific system for naming organisms uses a binomial nomenclature system. It is universal and consists of using the genus and species name for each.

3. Taxonomy is a hierarchical system used to classify living organisms and is made up of seven levels (from largest to smallest); Kingdom, Phylum, Class, Order, Family, Genus and Species.

4. The two main branches of taxonomy are cladistics and phenetics.

5. Species are the basic building block for evolution, and can be defined as organisms that are able to interbreed with one another to produce fertile offspring.

6. The six kingdoms of taxonomy are: Archaebacteria, Eubacteria, Protista, Fungi, Plantæ, and Animalia.

Notes

_____
_____
_____
_____
_____
_____
_____
_____
_____
_____
_____
_____
_____

Lesson #5 – Questions

1. Give 2 reasons why using an organism's common name is not clear enough for scientific communication.

_____

_____

_____

_____

_____

2. Describe convergent evolution. Why does this type of evolution tend to confuse scientists?

_____

_____

_____

_____

_____

3. Arrange the following categories in order from general to specific: genus, phylum, kingdom, species, order, family, class.

_____

_____

_____

_____

_____

4. How do the two main branches of taxonomy differ from one another?

_____

_____

_____

_____

_____

_____

Plants and Animals

Lesson #6 – The Plant Kingdom

Objectives:

- To describe adaptations made by plants for land survival

- To distinguish vascular from non-vascular plants

- To explain the significance of the development of the seed on success in different habitats

- To identify the differences between reproduction in gymnosperms and angiosperms

- To describe the role of the flower in angiosperms

- To define the roles of roots, shoots and leaves in plants

- To compare and contrast three types of plant tissue; vascular, ground and dermal

- To explain plant growth; primary and secondary

- To differentiate between fertilization and pollination

Introduction

As was briefly explained in the last lesson, organisms that are part of the Kingdom Plantae are multi-cellular, and the cells are organized into tissue that each performs a specialized function within the plant. The cells of all plants are eukaryotic and all contain chloroplasts so that plants can undergo photosynthesis and make their own food. Scientists also have enough evidence, from fossils, to believe that many of the plants we know today actually evolved from green algae, which is classified in the Kingdom Protista. This evolution means that plants had to adapt several features which would enable them to reproduce and survive in a terrestrial, as opposed to aquatic, habitat. This lesson will investigate the properties of the most common plants, such as trees, ferns, mosses and flowers.

Plant Adaptations for Terrestrial Habitats

Millions of years ago, as plants evolved from aquatic green algae, they had to make several adaptations to their structure so that they could successfully reproduce in a dry environment. There are three principle adaptations that needed to take place; reduced water loss, reproduction with little water, and absorption of minerals from soil.

First, a method of reducing water loss was required for the dry environment of the land. The plants with leaves that were covered in a waxy substance had a better chance of survival because this layer acted to prevent much of the evaporation that would have otherwise taken place. This waxy layer is known as the cuticle, and the leaves of most plants secrete this waxy substance naturally.

The second adaptation that was needed was a method of reproducing with little water available. This gave rise to tiny structures called spores and seeds, which could be carried by wind to different areas where reproduction was possible, perhaps where dew had settled.

The final adaptation was a means for plants to absorb nutrients through the soil. Fortunately, the Kingdom Fungi had already established itself on land, and plants were able to form a symbiotic relationship with the filaments of the fungi, leading to the creation of tiny structures called mycorrhizae. Mycorrhizae eventually evolved into roots. Finally, plants were able to reproduce successfully on land!

Plant Adaptations

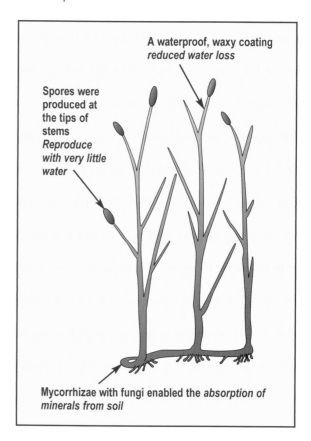

One characteristic that remained from green algae was the plants' ability to photosynthesize. Photosynthesis is the process whereby plants use carbon dioxide from the air, water from the soil and energy from the sun to produce glucose and oxygen. In order to do this, plant cells have organelles called chloroplasts which contain chlorophyll which allows the plants to harness the energy of the sun.

Equation for Photosynthesis

$$6\ H_2O + 6\ CO_2 \xrightarrow[\text{(solar energy)}]{+\ \text{sunlight}} 6\ O_2 + C_6H_{12}O_6$$

Plant Characteristics

There are several ways in which scientists group plants based on different characteristics. They can be grouped based on the presence of different structures such as vascular tissue, seeds, cotyledons, or flowers.

(a) Vascular vs. Non-vascular Plants

Vascular tissue can be compared to the circulatory or cardiovascular system in humans. It is the system of tubes in the plant that carry water and nutrients to every stem and every leaf. Plants that have vascular tissue are generally larger, taller, and more complex plants. After all, a small plant, close to the ground would have no use for tubes to deliver water, minerals and nutrients. However, think of one of the largest trees in the world, the sequoia tree. How is it possible that every leaf and stem on the tree receives water absorbed up to 80 meters below at the roots? The answer lies in the vascular system of the tree, which is able to pump water and nutrients throughout.

Vascular System

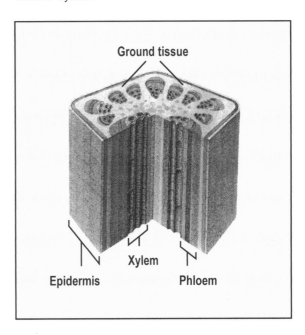

On the other hand, non-vascular plants, such as mosses, do not have this piping throughout because they grow low to the ground and are generally smaller in size. They use processes such as osmosis and diffusion to ensure that each part of the plant receives adequate water and nutrients. Osmosis is the process where water moves naturally from an area of low solute concentration to an area of high solute concentration. Diffusion is nearly the same process, only the nutrients themselves (such as sugar and minerals) move from an area of high concentration to an area of low concentration.

(b) Seed vs. Seedless Plants

Among vascular plants, there are those that produce seeds and those that do not. Those that produce seeds are able to thrive in much dryer and harsher conditions than those without because the protective covering around the seed prevents damage due to physical injury or drought. Seedless vascular plants, such as ferns and some mosses, are reasonably successful; however they are still some-what restricted to moister areas.

Both the spore (in seedless plants) and the seed contain an embryo which contains the necessary genetic information to produce a mature plant. Other than the hard, protective coat around the embryo, seed plants also have another feature which has contributed largely to their success – the cotyledon. This structure stores extra food and nutrients which are made available to the embryo upon germination (cracking of the seed for growth). Seeds can be dispersed in many ways, since some have hook, feather or even wing-like projections, and therefore have overcome most habitats.

Pictures of a Variety of Seeds and Spores

Seed with Wing

Dandelion Fuzz

Peach Pit

The last advantage that seed plants have over seedless plants is their development of woody tissue which provides strength so that the plant can grow very tall and can receive enough sunlight.

Woody Tissue

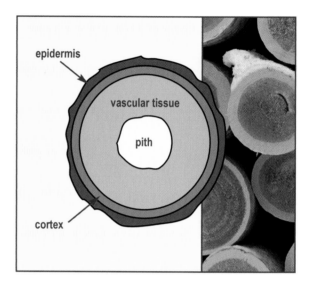

(c) Gymnosperms vs. Angiosperms

All seed plants can be further divided into two groups, gymnosperms or angiosperms. Gymnosperms are plants that don't produce flowers or fruit; they simply produce a 'naked' seed, usually in the form of a cone. Angiosperms are fruit and flower-bearing plants, where the seed is enclosed in the fruit.

The most common gymnosperms are coniferous trees like pine and spruce trees. These types of trees have two types of cones, seed cones and pollen cones. The seed cones carry the egg (female part of the genetic information), while the pollen cones carry the sperm (male part of the genetic information). In order for a new plant to grow, the sperm must reach the egg and fuse with it.

Coniferous Trees

Pollen Cone
(Male Cone)

Seed Cone
(Female Cone)

Angiosperms, such as maple trees or roses, produce flowers which help to ensure that the sperm gets transferred properly. The fruit which enclose the seed act as a means for protection of the seed. These two features of angiosperms are the main reasons for the success of the angiosperm; hence they have become the most abundant type of vascular plant.

Cactus

Tomatoes

Maple Leaves

Lilies

(d) Monocots vs. Dicots

Angiosperms can be divided even further into either monocots or dicots, names which indicate the number of cotyledons present in the seed. Monocots have only one cotyledon, while dicots have two. Other than this main feature, monocots have some other traits which set them apart.

Monocots, such as lilies and palms, have leaf veins which are parallel and their flowers always have petals in multiples of three. Upon closer examination, the vascular tissue of monocots is quite scattered within the stem.

Dicots, such as shrubs and trees, have leaf veins which branch from one another, while their flowers have petals in multiples of four or five. Unlike monocots, their vascular tissue is arranged in a circular form around the stem. (See the diagram on the next page.)

	Monocots	Dicots
Cotyledons	1	2
Leaf Veins	parallel	like a net
Flower	petals multiples of 3	petals multiples of 4 or 5
Vascular Tissue	scattered	circular

Plants / Tree Diagram

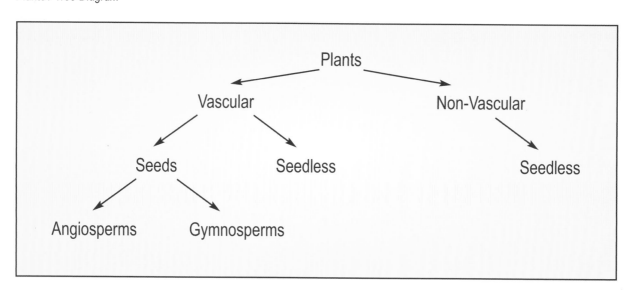

Plant Structure

All plants must have very specialized structures for their particular environments, because they are not mobile like their fellow counterparts in the Kingdom Animalia. They must be able to absorb nutrients and water, even when both are sparing. They must also be able to receive enough sunlight in order to produce food to sustain them, and they must also be able to protect themselves from predators. All of these tasks are heavily dependent on their structure.

(a) Plant Body – Roots, Stem & Leaves

The main purpose of the roots is to absorb water and nutrients from the soil. In order to assist with this monumental task, there exist tiny little structures called root hairs. They are much smaller than the roots themselves, and can therefore reach in between molecules of soil to maximize absorption of water and nutrients. Root hairs also maximize the surface area for absorption which also helps. Roots also serve as the anchor for the plant. This protects the plant against harsh conditions such as rain, wind and even against animals or humans as they may

Roots

try to pull it from the Earth. Roots have a third and very important function in plants – growth, but we will discuss this in the next section.

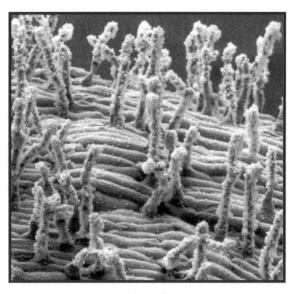

Root Hairs

The stem and leaves together make up a structure which scientists refer to as the plant shoot. The primary function of the stem is to place the plant leaves in a position where they can receive the maximum amount of sunlight that they require in order to photosynthesize. The stem is also the part of the plant which contains the vascular tissue, or the piping, of the plant.

The leaves main function is photosynthesis. They are generally thin and flat so that they have a large surface area with which to 'catch' sunlight. As a secondary function, but crucial to the survival of the plant, they also control the amount of water that is released from the plant. Due to the presence of tiny pores in leaves, called stomata, they are able to regulate how much water is released. When water is released from a plant, it is called transpiration. In a drought, the leaves must conserve as much water as possible, and so the stomata remain closed.

Leaves with Stomata

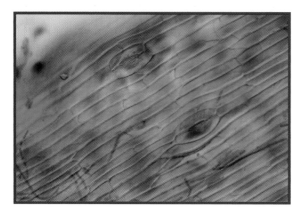

Stomata Close-Up

Types of Plant Tissue

(a) Vascular Tissue

The vascular tissue of a plant is made up of two main structures; the xylem and the phloem. Xylem is the tubing that carries and distributes water to the entire plant. Phloem is similar, but it carries the minerals, sugars and other nutrients that the plant needs to every part of the plant.

You may be wondering how the water and nutrients travel upwards in the plant or tree, when the force of gravity should be forcing it downwards. There are three methods which allow water to move against the force of gravity: osmosis, capillary action and cohesion of water molecules. As you learned earlier, osmosis is the movement of water and it occurs from the soil into the plant, at the roots. From there, capillary action takes over. This moves the water upwards due to the strong attraction of the water molecules to the sides of the xylem tubing. The final method of moving water upwards in a plant occurs due to the cohesion of water molecules. Water molecules are powerfully attracted to one another, and so when water is being evaporated from the leaves (transpiration), the water molecules 'stick' to one another and hence get pulled up towards the leaves.

Diagram of Capillary Action, Cohesion of Water Molecules

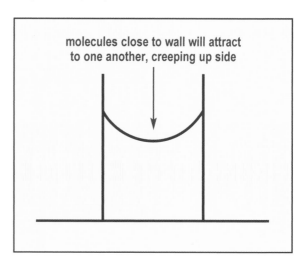

molecules close to wall will attract
to one another, creeping up side

If you are sceptical about just how strong is the cohesion between water molecules, you could try the following experiment at home. Take a small cup and fill it to the brim with water. Then, carefully and slowly, add one penny at a time to the full glass. As you add the pennies, watch the formation of water at the top of the glass – it becomes almost bubble-like and won't spill because the water molecules hold on to each other. This is water cohesion at work.

The phloem moves nutrients in a similar way, but the movement of nutrients in plants is given a special name called translocation. The movement occurs partially due to diffusion, but the phloem is also under great pressure and this helps the flow of nutrients.

(b) Ground Tissue

Ground tissue is all the material that surrounds the vascular tissue. Its main function is to store water and carbohydrates until the plant needs them. In doing this, it is providing pressure and support to the stem, making it rigid and capable of standing tall. This pressure is called turgor pressure, and without it, the plant wilts and dies.

Rigid Plant

Wilted Plant

(c) Dermal Tissue

Dermal tissue forms the outer layer of the plant called the epidermis. These cells surround the plant and form the skin of the plant. They produce the waxy cuticle which protects the plant from losing too much water.

Plant Growth

Plant growth occurs at regions called meristems. Meristems are regions where cells undergo division, in order to generate more cells. The cells that are produced at these regions go on and differentiate into the many different types of cells that are required for the plant to function. Some may become part of the vasculature, while some may become epidermal cells, while others might develop into ground tissue cells. The important thing to recognize is that every time a cell divides, one goes on to become a different type of cell, but one always remains behind as a meristem cell, so the process can continue.

There are two types of growth: primary and secondary. Primary growth occurs mainly at the root tips and causes the plant to get longer in both directions. Secondary growth causes an increase to the breadth or thickness of the plant.

Both types of growth are initiated at meristems. (See the diagram on top of page 136.)

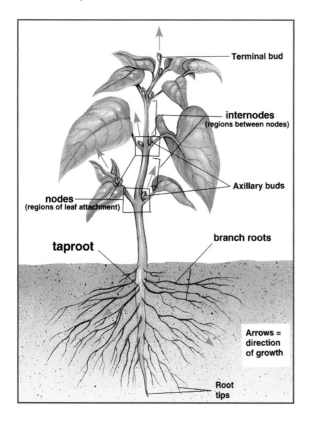

Cells at Meristem

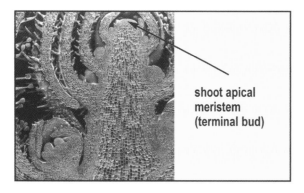

shoot apical meristem (terminal bud)

Plant Reproduction

In order for reproduction to occur, in either gymnosperms or angiosperms, two processes must first happen. The first is pollination, which is simply the delivery of the pollen, which contains the sperm, from its production site to the location of the egg. The second thing which must occur is fertilization, which is the fusion of the sperm and the egg. Fertilization can occur days, weeks or months after pollination occurs, and produces a seed which can then be transported to a good place for growth.

(a) Gymnosperms

In general, gymnosperms are wind-pollinated. This means that each of the pollen grains from the pollen cones are carried by the wind to the site of the fallen seed cones. This process is made easier by two tiny air sacs attached to each single grain of pollen, which help carry the pollen further than it would without the air sacs. Usually this process occurs on lakes, or smaller bodies of water such as ponds or even puddles.

Accumulated Pollen

(b) Angiosperms

In angiosperms, the sperm and the egg are both found within the same flower, but are different structures. There is only one female structure per flower and it is called the pistil, and is composed of three parts: the stigma, the style and the ovary. The ovary contains the ovule (egg), and is

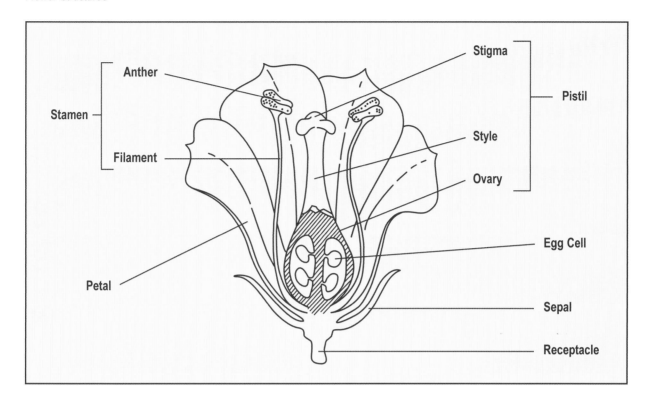

the site of fertilization. There are several male structures found around the pistil, called stamens. Each stamen consists of a filament and an anther. The anther is where the pollen, containing the sperm, is produced.

Unlike gymnosperms, angiosperms are not always pollinated by the wind, although they can be. Sometimes they self-pollinate. This occurs when the pollen from the anther simply falls onto the stigma and makes its way down the style to the ovary. In this case, the resulting plants will be identical copies of the original. In most cases, however, it is insects and animals that complete pollination of angiosperms. They are attracted to the bright colors of the flowers, or the sweet scents of some, and as they approach to investigate or feed,

they collect some pollen from the anthers on their bodies. As they fly from flower to flower, some of the pollen gets deposited on the stigmas of other flowers and the result is called cross-pollination. Cross-pollination occurs when the pollen from one flower gets transferred to another and this ensures genetic recombination or variety among plants.

Seed Dispersal

The final step, once fertilization has occurred and a new seed has been produced, in both gymnosperms and angiosperms is for the seed to be put somewhere where it can grow and mature. Seeds can be dispersed in a variety of methods; wind, water, birds, animals, insects, and even humans. One of the reasons seed plants have been so successful is because during the dispersal, the seed coat protects the embryo from injury. Many little animals can be caught searching and moving seeds around from place to place. In the case of angiosperms, animals eat the fruit and seed, then pass it through their digestive tract and deposit it elsewhere in their feces. Have you ever eaten a plum or a peach, or even an apple and then tossed the pit into the forest? You too may have already completed the process of reproduction in seed plants.

Lesson Summary

1. Plants underwent several adaptations in order to survive in terrestrial habitats.

2. Some larger plants have a vascular system to distribute water and nutrients to all its parts.

3. Some plants produce seeds, while others produce spores instead.

4. Seed plants can be divided into two categories: gymnosperms (non-flowering or fruit-bearing) and angiosperms (flowering and fruit-bearing).

5. Angiosperms can be further divided into monocots and dicots.

6. The body of a plant is made up of roots, a stem and leaves.

7. There are three types of plant tissue: vascular, ground and dermal.

8. Water and nutrients reach each part of the plant through a variety of methods: osmosis, diffusion, capillary action, water cohesion and translocation.

9. Plant reproduction involves pollination and fertilization.

10. Gymnosperms and angiosperms reproduce in slightly different manners.

Notes

_____

_____

_____

_____

_____

_____

_____

_____

Lesson #6 – Questions

1. Why did marine plants require so many adaptations to be successful land-dwellers? What were those adaptations?

_____

_____

_____

_____

_____

_____

_____

_____

2. What means do plants rely on for moving water from roots to leaves, against the direction of gravity?

_____

_____

_____

_____

_____

_____

_____

_____

_____

3. Both gymnosperms and angiosperms require pollination. What is pollination and how is it different in these plant types? Which is more successful?

_____

_____

_____

_____

_____

_____

_____

_____

$\Rightarrow$

Lesson #6 – Questions (continued)

4. Describe the difference between cross-pollination and self-pollination.

_____

_____

_____

_____

_____

_____

_____

_____

_____

_____

_____

_____

_____

_____

_____

5. Explain why the development of the seed was a major factor in the success of plants.

_____

_____

_____

_____

_____

_____

_____

_____

_____

_____

_____

_____

_____

_____

_____

_____

Lesson #7 – The Animal Kingdom

Objectives:

- To list the three common characteristics of all animals

- To understand the importance of multi-cellularity, specialization of cells and formation of tissues and organs

- To describe various types of body cavities; acoelomate, pseudocoelomate and coelomate

- To outline the general path of evolution beginning with the multi-cellular protists and ending with various phyla

- To explain some of the adaptations that took place in order for animals to move from aquatic to terrestrial environments

- To describe the various phyla of Kingdom Animalia

- To describe the major classes of the phylum Chordata

Introduction

As with plants, the very first animal species existed in marine environments. Through a long evolution, animals now exist in nearly every environment on Earth. The diversity of the animal kingdom is largely due to the process of natural selection, whereby organisms possessing desirable characteristics survive and are able to reproduce. This lesson will examine characteristics that are common to all animals, as well as many that have been specially derived to suit the needs of the animal in its particular living environment. Some of these characteristics include body cavities, development of limbs, waterproof skin as well as a means of exchanging gas in a dry environment. Furthermore, we will investigate the properties of all the major phyla and some classes of the animal kingdom.

Evolution of Animal Characteristics

Based on fossil evidence, it is likely that all animals evolved from an early heterotrophic protist in a marine environment, the ocean. There are three characteristics which are common to all animals today, although some characteristics have evolved significantly more in some than others.

Firstly, all animals are heterotrophic, meaning that they are not able to produce their own food, and are consumers. Secondly, all animals are multi-cellular, meaning that they are made up of more than one cell. Multi-cellular organisms are more complex than unicellular organisms because their cells are specialized to carry out specific functions in the body. Thirdly, animal cells do not have a cell wall.

Imagine being the CEO of a major company. It would be very difficult to oversee every aspect of the company, and so to make your job easier, you would hire managers to supervise and specialize in certain areas of the company; accounting, marketing, public relations, advertising, manufacturing, distribution and sales. The same thing has occurred in cells due to specialization. Cell specialization provides an advantage to multi-cellular organisms because it means that not every cell has to carry out every function, there exists division of labor.

As a result of specialization, tissues arose. A tissue is a group of cells organized into a coordinated and functional unit, just as the sales manager at a major company would have an entire team to assist with the coordination of sales. Muscle tissue is formed by a group of cells which are able to contract so as to produce movement. Nervous tissue is able to transmit electrical signals so that body parts can communicate with one another.

Tissues were the evolutionary result of a process called gastrulation. Gastrulation is the formation of layers of cells and occurs in the developing embryos of all animals except sponges (phylum Porifera). It occurs when the outermost layer of cells in an organism is pinched inwards, and the inner fold of membrane seals off, so that an outer and an inner membrane now exist. The outer membrane is known as the ectoderm, while the inner membrane is known as the endoderm.

Diagram of Gastrulation Process

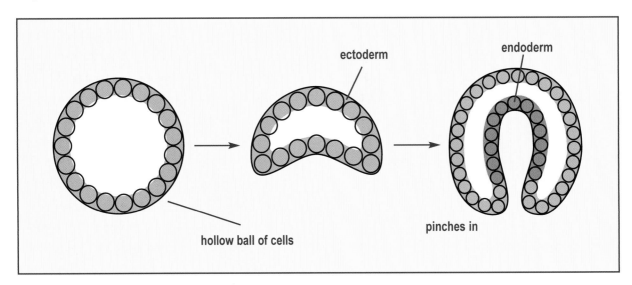

144 | BIOLOGY | Unit Two

The ectoderm always gives rise to the same type of tissues, the skin and/or the nervous tissue. The endoderm usually gives rise to tissue that forms the lining of the gut (tube in which digestion of food occurs). Organisms that are part of phylum Cnidaria, like jelly fish and sea anemones, were some of the first organisms to have both types of tissues. In essence, the bodies of these types of animals look like a double-layered sac of cells.

Diagram of the Cnidaria Body Type

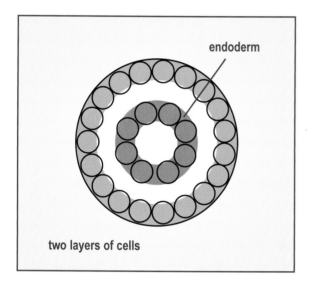

A third layer of tissue, the mesoderm, made its appearance first in the phylum Platyhelminthes, in organisms such as flatworms. Once gastrulation has occurred, the mesoderm is a group of cells that forms in the space between the endoderm and the ectoderm, in the embryo. The mesoderm tissue layer most often gives rise to muscle, reproductive, and circulatory organs.

Diagram of the Formation of the Mesoderm

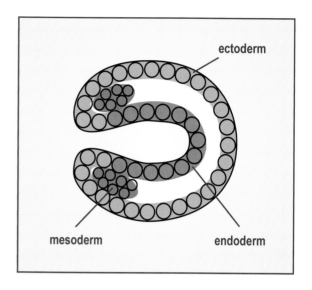

Organs are groups of tissues that are responsible for carrying out one function, and are generally grouped into a system of organs that work together to carry out and perform a function. For example, in humans, the liver, the pancreas, the gall bladder, stomach and intestines are all organs which work together to accomplish the process of digestion. Individually, they each have their own specific function, but together, these organs are known as the digestive system.

As is becoming evident, the introduction of the three layers of cells in embryos led to the formation of various tissues, which in turn led to the formation of organs, and finally systems, in mature organisms. As the number of layers increased to three, the organism itself, became much more complex because cells were able to perform very specialized functions. These layers also resulted in different types of body designs.

Body Design Features

One of the most interesting features of the animal kingdom is the amount of physical diversity among its entire species. As the development of tissues progressed, so did the shape and design of the bodies of various organisms.

(a) Symmetry

Symmetry exists if you can cut along one axis of an object or organism so that the resulting two pieces are identical in nature. Think about your own body's symmetry compared to that of a hydra or a jellyfish. Jellyfish have a different type of symmetry than humans. They exhibit radial symmetry, which means that if

Jellyfish / Radially Symmetrical Organism

Human and Dog / Bilaterally Symmetrical Organism

a cross-section is taken, both halves will be identical. This is very different then most other animals, which exhibit bilateral symmetry instead. Bilateral symmetry exists when you can make a cut from top to bottom along the front of an organism to produce identical pieces. For instance, flatworms, turtles, dogs and humans are bilaterally symmetrical because they have two eyes, two front and two back limbs, two lungs, etc. Bilateral symmetry is characteristic of more complex animals, and was first observed in the phylum Platyhelminthes.

(b) Cephalisation

Most bilaterally symmetrical animals also have a head and tail, whereas animals that are radially symmetrical do not. The process of evolving head and tail ends is known as cephalisation. The presence of a head is the primary result of the creation of sensory organs, as well as a processing organ, the brain. Because of the development of sensory organs on the head end, these types of organisms also tend to move about through their environments.

Their acoelomate body plan requires that they be thin in order to allow substances to pass easily to all organs.

Flatworm

(c) Two-way vs. One-way Gut

Organisms that have only one opening from the interior to exterior of their bodies must ingest and excrete materials from the same place, hence this is known as a two-way gut. The flow of materials in and out of the body at the same time results in a less efficient digestive system, and it is more difficult for nutrients to be absorbed properly. A one-way digestive system is far more efficient at absorbing nutrients because the flow of materials is only going in one direction.

(d) Segmentation

The one feature of body design that has proved to be one of the most successful in the animal kingdom is segmentation. A segmented body is divided into repeated body units, where each segment or unit can actually have a different function. Some organisms that display segmentation are from the phyla Annelids (earthworms), Arthropods (insects) and Chordata (vertebrates). It is easy to see the segments on an earthworm, and even on insects, however it is more difficult in vertebrates, such as humans. The human spinal cord is an example of segmentation, as are muscles.

The earthworm is an annelid. Members of this phylum have segmented bodies.

Earthworm

Body Cavities

The final, and perhaps most significant, distinction between types of animals lies in the structure of their body cavities. There are three types of body cavities: acoelomate, pseudocoelomate, and coelomate.

(a) Acoelomate

Acoelomates are organisms, like the flatworm, that do not have a body cavity. The mesoderm grows solidly between the ectoderm and endoderm. This limits their structure to thin and small because it is more difficult for diffusion of nutrients and osmosis to occur through solids than open space. Because of this, the digestive systems of acoelomates are often branched in order to be close to the surface.

(b) Pseudocoelomates

A pseudocoelomate is an organism with a cavity between the mesoderm and the endoderm. This type of cavity permits relatively simple diffusion of nutrients to the rest of the body, and so bodies can be somewhat thicker and longer if necessary, such as the roundworm from the phylum Nematoda.

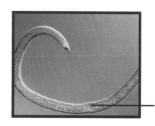
The roundworms have a body cavity, the pseudocoelom. They are not packed with solid tissues as are the flatworms. The pseudocoelom allows for more efficient diffusion of nutrients to body organs.

Roundworm

(c) Coelomates

Most animals have a coelom, which means a true body cavity. This type of cavity is located within the mesoderm and provides some advantages to the organism. One advantage is that this type of cavity provides insulation to the organs because it is fluid-filled. The second major advantage is that the coelom allows the gut to function independently of the body wall and therefore can be much longer than the organism, which is better for absorption of nutrients.

Land Adaptations

Due to the adaptations made by some phyla, these organisms were able to relocate from their marine habitats to terrestrial habitats, becoming far more diverse in nature. Sponges, Cnidarians (jelly fish and relatives) and Echinoderms (sea stars and relatives) were left at sea because they failed to make the necessary adaptations for life on land, while every other phyla in the animal kingdom can be found on land. Except for Arthropods (insects),

and Vertebrates, most phyla require a relatively moist area for successful life. The following section outlines some of the major adaptations made by most land-dwelling organisms.

(a) Physical Support

In moving to land, many organisms had to overcome the loss of physical support that was provided by water which surrounded them. Because water is far denser than air, it provided an enormous amount of support to the bodies of animals which might otherwise collapse under the force of gravity. It was likely the development of the skeleton and limbs with joints was the major adaptation which not only provided physical support, but also allowed the animals to literally climb out of their marine habitats and explore land. It is believed that most land animals have a common ancestor in the lobe-finned fish, which likely evolved to what we know

Diagrams of the Three Different Types of Cavities

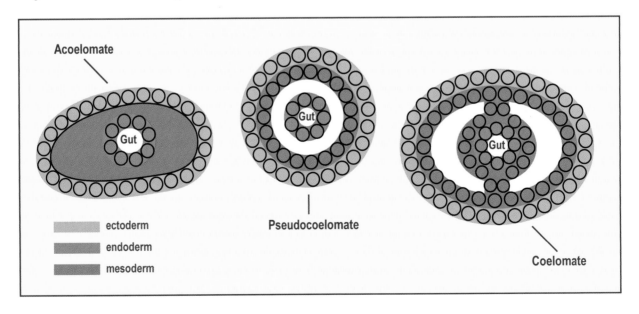

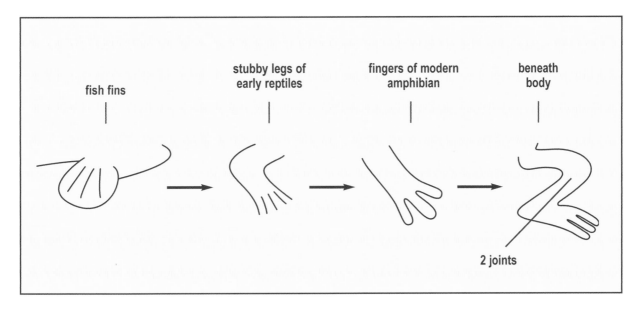

as amphibians and then on to reptiles. Fossil evidence shows the evolution of the limbs of these three types of organisms. Notice in the diagram above how the limbs of reptiles are placed more below the body which provides more effective support.

(b) Hearing Mechanisms for Air

Sound vibrations travel much faster and further in water than in air due to the proximity of water molecules compared to that of air molecules. As animals began to appear on land, the ones that were able to hear sounds had a definite advantage over those that could not. This lead to the evolution of structures which enabled sounds to be amplified or better detected. Some animals developed ears, which would amplify sounds and direct them to the inner ear, while other animals developed other features such as ultra-sensitive hairs, membranes, which let them feel sounds as opposed to hearing them.

Cricket

Snake

Orangutan

Insect

Lizard

Human

(c) Waterproof Skin

One major accomplishment of the land-adapted animals was the acquisition of a waterproof skin that minimized water loss due to evaporation. Without this watertight skin, too much water could be lost and organisms would simply dry up and die. Insects have developed one of the best waterproof exteriors called an exoskeleton. This exoskeleton is a tough coat made of waxes and a material called chitin. Reptiles have developed scales, and humans have developed skin.

(d) Breathing

Both marine and terrestrial animals must absorb oxygen and rid their cells of carbon dioxide, but gas exchange structures such as gills, which work well in water, would not be able to withstand the force of gravity. Many animals have adapted by developing lungs; organs which have a large moist surface area interfaced with a delivery system (circulatory system) where diffusion of oxygen and carbon dioxide can happen quickly. Other animals, such as insects, have developed tracheae which are tubes connected to pores on the outside of their bodies, which allow oxygen and carbon dioxide to be exchanged directly.

(e) Reproduction on Land

For sexual reproduction to occur, the sperm and the egg must unite in a moist area. This suits fish and amphibians well because they fertilize their eggs externally in the water that surrounds them. However, in order for land animals to fertilize their eggs, the solution was internal fertilization. Internal fertilization simply means that the sperm meets the egg inside the female. For reptiles and birds, the difference is that the egg doesn't mature inside the female. Instead, an egg is laid and the embryo grows outside of the mother surrounded by a waterproof shell that still allows gas exchange to occur. The eggs of mammals do not have shells and the embryo develops completely inside the mother.

Major Phyla

There are nine major phyla of the animal kingdom and their names, characteristics and some examples are provided in the following summary table.

Jellyfish / Cnidaria

Bird / Chordata

Major Phyla

Phylum Name	General Characteristics	Example Organisms
Porifera	• Marine habitat – attach to hard surfaces • Asymmetrical • Ectoderm only • Can reproduce sexually or asexually	• Sponges
Cnidaria	• Marine habitat – have large stinging structures around one body opening • Radially symmetrical • Have ectoderm and endoderm	• Jellyfish • Sea anemones
Platyhelminthes	• Live in water or moist areas • Acoelomate • Bilaterally symmetrical • Have undergone cephalization • Unprotected against water loss • Can reproduce sexually or asexually • Generally parasitic (require host)	• All flatworms (eg. tapeworms)
Nematoda	• Aquatic habitats usually • Reproduces sexually • Pseudocoelomate • Some are parasitic	• All roundworms
Mollusca	• Aquatic and terrestrial habitats • Usually have shells • Coelomate • Presence of circulatory system	• Clams • Snails • Mussels • Octopuses
Annelida	• Segmentation • Bilaterally symmetrical • Coelomate • Some are parasitic, some are helpful	• Earthworms • Leeches
Arthropoda	• Presence of exoskeleton • Jointed limbs • Most abundant phylum	• Spiders • Centipedes • Insects • Shrimp and crabs
Echinodermata	• Show 5-part radial symmetry • Marine habitats • Coelomate	• Sea stars • Sea cucumbers
Chordata	• Most diverse phylum	• Human • Lancelets • Snakes • Birds • Tunicates • Frogs

Lesson Summary

1. The three common characteristics of animals are heterotrophy, multi-cellularity, and no cell wall.

2. The body of an animal can have a variety of features; radial or bilateral symmetry, cephalisation, one or two-way gut, or segmentation.

3. The body cavity of an animal can be one of three types: acoelomate, pseudocoelomate or coelomate.

4. The major adaptations that sea animals underwent for land were: development of limbs, structures for hearing, waterproof skin, gas exchange systems, and means for internal fertilization.

5. The major phyla of the animal kingdom are: Porifera, Cnidaria, Platyhelminthes, Nematoda, Mollusca, Annelida, Arthropods, Echinodermata, and Chordata.

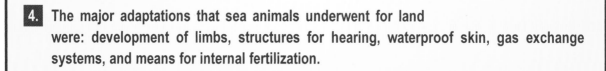
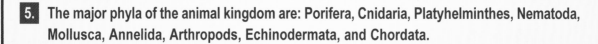

Notes

_____
_____
_____
_____
_____
_____
_____
_____
_____
_____
_____
_____
_____
_____
_____
_____

Lesson #7 – Questions

1. Contrast and compare two types of body cavities and then two types of symmetries. Which of each has been more successful and why?

_____

_____

_____

_____

_____

2. Cell specialization is largely due to the formation of different types of tissue during the process of gastrulation. Name each type of tissue, and what it gives rise to.

_____

_____

_____

_____

_____

3. Name three adaptations that marine animals had to make in order to move to land.

_____

_____

_____

_____

_____

_____

4. Name and give two major characteristics of each animal kingdom.

_____

_____

_____

_____

_____

CHEMISTRY UNIT 3

Matter and the Changes in Matter

Lesson #1 – Matter, Energy, and the Classification of Matter

Introduction

Take a minute to look around you. You are surrounded by stuff – a wooden table, a glass window, a sunset, a computer printer, a cardboard box, a cup of water, a metal picture frame, a wax candle, a plastic container, a pile of paper, a cotton blanket, a balloon filled with helium, a woollen sweater, a leather handbag, a sandy beach, even the clouds in the sky.

What is this stuff?

computer

water

window

wooden table

What about the stuff that we cannot see or touch, but that we know is there? For instance, a fireplace can be lit and within minutes we can feel a nice warm sensation in our bodies – heat. The flick of a simple switch upon entering a room can eliminate darkness – light. We can't see light or heat,

but we know they are there because they work for us and make our everyday lives much more manageable.

Where did all of this stuff come from, what is it made of and how can each item have such different properties? Believe it or not, all of these beautiful landscapes, useful objects and things that we take for granted everyday are due to interactions between the various types of chemicals found on Earth. In this lesson we will examine the difference between matter and energy, investigate different types of matter and learn to identify the three different states of matter.

Matter

Matter is the physical material that makes up the universe. Since all matter takes up space, it must have mass and volume. All matter is made up of tiny particles. Mass is a measure of the amount of particles that make up a substance, while volume is a measure of how much space a substance occupies. Scientists are very curious and spend much of their time trying to measure matter. They want to measure things like mass, length, volume, density and speed of matter. Measurements play a very important role in the understanding of matter.

In order for scientists all around the world to communicate with one another, a system that allows them to use the same units of measurement in every country has been adopted. This system is called the metric system. It is based on units of measurement that are expressed as multiples of 10, 100, 1000, and so on, of the base unit. The gram (g) is the base unit for mass, the meter (m) is the base unit for length, while the litre (L) is the base unit for volume. A series of prefixes is used to express different quantities of each measurement. For example, if you want to measure a really large distance, e.g. New York to Los Angeles, you wouldn't use meters (m), you would use kilometers (km). The prefix kilo means one thousand meters. Prefixes are also useful when measuring very small quantities. If you wanted to measure the volume of a raindrop, you would not use liters (L), you would use milliliters (mL). The prefix milli means one thousandth of a litre. It is very important to be able to convert between the different units when solving problems.

In addition to mass, length and volume, there is another commonly used measurement called density. Density is a measure of how much "stuff" can fit into a particular space. Density is calculated by dividing an object's mass by its volume. The base unit of measurement for density is g/mL. For example, if you have a volume of 2 mL of water and it has a mass of 2 g, then water has a density of 1 g/mL.

Density Formula $D = M/V$

Density can also explain the behavior of certain substances with one another. For instance, the density of olive oil is approximately 0.92 g/mL, less than that of water. When water and oil are mixed, they separate and oil always ends up on top. This is because it has a lower density than water, therefore floating above it.

Prefix Chart

Prefix	# of Bases Units	Examples
mega	10^6	megaliter
kilo	10^3	kilogram
BASE UNIT	1	meter
deci	10^{-1}	decimeter
centi	10^{-2}	centigram
milli	10^{-3}	milliliter
micro	10^{-6}	microgram

Energy

In contrast to matter, *energy* does not have mass and does not occupy space. Another property of energy is that it can not be created or destroyed – it can only be transferred from one place to another. For example, when a light switch is turned on, electrical energy is converted to light and heat energy. The electrical energy is not destroyed. This is known as *The Law of Conservation of Energy*. Energy is critical to matter and to living systems because it allows us to do work.

There are two basic types of energy; kinetic and potential. Kinetic energy is the result of the movement of particles in matter. For example, heat is a form of kinetic energy because when an object is hot the particles that make up the object are moving much more quickly than when it is cold. Potential energy is a result of the position of an object in space, and has the ability to do work. In science, we define work as the ability to move a force through a distance. For instance, a rock lying on the face of the Earth has no potential energy, but if you were to hold the rock above your head, your muscles would transfer potential energy to the rock. The rock now has the ability to do work, whereas before it did not. If the rock is dropped, potential energy becomes kinetic energy.

There are several different forms of kinetic (K) and potential (P) energy that we are familiar with in our daily lives – nuclear energy, solar energy, wind energy, heat energy, light energy, electrical energy and wave energy. Think about each type of energy that was mentioned, can you determine if it is kinetic or potential energy?

electrical energy

heat energy

solar energy

wind energy

Albert Einstein uncovered a formula that would forever describe the relationship between energy and matter. E is the amount of energy, m is the mass, and c is the speed of light.

Energy Formula	$E = mc^2$

Using this equation, we can determine the amount of energy held within a substance of any mass. However, only a small portion of this enormous amount of energy can be released in nuclear reactions, under a very limited set of circumstances.

DID YOU KNOW?
Our Sun is "burning" hydrogen to make helium. As a result of this reaction, some matter is lost and converted to energy. Every second there is a loss in the mass of the Sun of 4 x 10⁹ kg. There is enough released energy to keep 30 100-W light bulbs lit for 10,000 years. The Sun has a mass of 2 x 10³⁰ kg and it is not ready to disappear for a while.

The Particle Theory of Matter

The Particle Theory of Matter is a scientific model used to explain how matter is organized and how it behaves when a change in temperature is observed. The Particle Theory of Matter states that:

1. All matter is made up of very small particles.

2. Each pure substance has a specific type of particle, different from particles of other substances.

3. Particles are attracted to one another depending how close together they are.

4. Particles are constantly in motion.

5. Generally, particles at high temperatures move faster than particles at lower temperatures.

Let's use the Particle Theory of Matter to further explore how water particles can be organized into the three physical states of matter; solid (ice), liquid (water), and gas (steam).

In the first diagram, the particles of the solid ice are very close together because they do not have enough kinetic energy to spread apart. The attraction forces between particles in a solid are so strong that the particles are held together in a definite shape and volume. This tight formation is called a lattice. In the second diagram, the water particles have enough kinetic energy to move around one another, but not enough to fully overcome their attractive forces. This is what gives all liquids their ability to "pour". Liquids have a definite volume, but no definite shape. Finally, in the third diagram, the water vapor particles have significant kinetic energy to be able to overcome the attractive forces between particles. One of the main properties of all gases is that they will fill any volume of space available. Even if your bicycle tire is full of air, it is always possible to add more air because there is so much space between gas particles, they can just squeeze tighter together, thereby occupying any volume.

When an ice cube is melted, or when water is boiled, matter is being changed.

Three Physical States of Matter

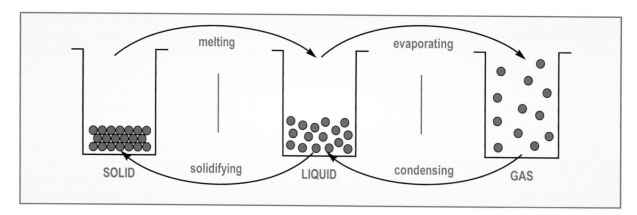

These are examples of a physical change or change of state. During a physical change the actual particles of matter are not being altered, so a new substance is not being created. Physical changes of matter are reversible, through methods such as melting or freezing. When water freezes, the particles that make up water do not change. These particles are called molecules and each water molecule looks the same as each molecule of ice – H_2O (2 hydrogen, 1 oxygen).

ice cube melting

liquid forming steam

log burning

rust forming

In contrast, when matter changes so that it forms a completely new substance and that change is non-reversible, scientists call this a chemical change. The chemical composition of the particles of matter has been changed permanently. An example of a chemical change is when a piece of wood is burned, the particles of wood are chemically changing into ash and smoke as new substances are formed.

Sometimes deciding whether or not a change in matter is chemical or physical can be difficult. Here are some clues to help you decide. If any of the following observations are made, it is likely that a *chemical change* took place:

• The temperature of the substance changes (on its own)

• There is a color change

• A material with new properties forms

• Gas bubbles are produced

• The starting material is used up

Classification of Matter

Niagara Falls   *Nile*

All matter can be classified into two main groups: pure substances or mixtures.

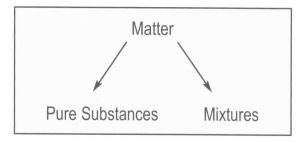

Pure substances are made of only one type of particle. Each particle may be composed of one or more smaller components, but always in a constant ratio. For instance, water is H_2O, which means that each particle of water is made of two hydrogens and one oxygen. Water is never composed of three hydrogens and two oxygens. Scientists use a term called **homogeneous** to describe substances where each particle is identical. Also, pure substances always have the same chemical and physical properties in every situation. Water taken from Niagara Falls or the Nile will be composed of two hydrogens and one oxygen, and will have a boiling point of 100°c.

Mixtures are combinations of pure substances that do not always have a fixed ratio of their components. For example, a beach contains many different types of sand in no particular ratio. A sample taken from one end of the beach could be completely different from a sample taken at the other end of the same beach. This beach would be considered a mechanical mixture. Scientists refer to mechanical mixtures as **heterogeneous**. However, mixtures are not always random. For example, table vinegar is a mixture of acetic acid and water, but if you were to sample two different bottles you would find that they had the same composition. This type of homogeneous mixture is called a solution.

Tree Diagram of Matter

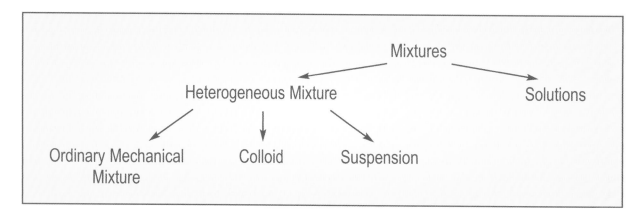

A heterogeneous mixture can be classified as a suspension, a colloid, or an ordinary mechanical mixture.

In a suspension, the particles can be seen and will eventually settle to the bottom due to gravity. For instance, orange juice with lots of pulp is a suspension because you must shake it before drinking. A colloid is similar to a suspension, however the particles in a colloid are so tiny that gravity will not cause them to settle at the bottom, so they remain suspended. Some examples of colloids are milk, whipping cream, and glue. The example of the beach would be that of an ordinary mechanical mixture.

beach / ordinary mechanical mixture

glue / colloid

milk / colloid

orange juice / suspension

Lesson Summary

1. Everything in the universe can be classified as either matter or energy. Matter is the physical material that has mass and occupies space, while energy gives matter the ability to do work, and cannot be seen or touched.

2. Scientists quantify matter using the metric system.

3. When matter changes, it is either a physical change of state, or a chemical reaction. A physical change does not alter the composition of the substance and is reversible, while a chemical change results in a new substance and is non-reversible.

4. Matter can be classified as either a mixture or a pure substance.

Notes

_____

_____

_____

_____

_____

_____

_____

_____

_____

_____

_____

_____

_____

_____

_____

_____

_____

_____

_____

Lesson #1 – Questions

1. What is the difference between matter and energy?

_____

_____

_____

_____

_____

2. Draw a tree diagram to indicate the relationships between mixtures, colloids, suspensions, pure substances, heterogeneous mechanical mixtures, and ordinary mechanical mixtures. The title of this diagram is "Matter".

3. Give an example of a chemical and physical change. What are some of the characteristics you used to make your decision?

_____

_____

_____

_____

_____

4. Calculate the density of an object with a mass of 50g, and a volume of 10mL.

_____

_____

_____

_____

_____

Lesson #2 – Atoms and Their Subatomic Particles

Objectives:

- To have a basic understanding of the scientific method

- To describe the various events leading to Dalton's model of the atom

- To explain Dalton's atomic theory and understand how it is different from the Particle Theory of Matter

- To explain the major experiments leading to the discovery of subatomic particles

- To identify the differences between a proton, neutron and electron

- To label a diagram of the modern-day structure of the atom

Introduction

Imagine two trains of thought; "thinkers" and "doers". Which one are you? If you are even the slightest bit scientifically minded, you probably have some of both qualities. Today though, we typically think of science as being a hands-on subject. Believe it or not, it wasn't always so.

Many centuries ago, science was thought of as a discipline in which careful thought and consideration was given on many topics, but where experimentation was rarely part of the process. "Thinkers" were called philosophers, and they were responsible for laying the foundation for many of the scientific theories and laws that we hold as truth today. However, without "doers", the alchemists, the importance of experimentation in science may have gone unnoticed. Unfortunately, neither group was perfect.

The Philosophers and Alchemists

The philosophers were a very academic, scholarly group and had many brilliant ideas about how things worked. The problem was that they were not open to discussion, and generally what they determined to be fact was accepted by the general population. This did not leave much room for the evolution of ideas or debate, and hence left the scientific community and the general public limited in their understanding of things around them.

On the other hand, the alchemists were busy experimenting, testing ideas and making discoveries of which they didn't want to share with anyone. This lack of cooperation among the alchemists and others hindered scientific progress because many of the same experiments were being repeated with no means of generating a larger body of knowledge.

Finally, a man by the name of Sir Francis Bacon came along in the late 1500's and managed to convince the scientific community that "thinking", "doing" and most of all sharing were necessary aspects of what would be forever coined the scientific method. As will be outlined in this lesson, the *scientific method* played an extraordinary role in better understanding the characteristics and structure of matter around us.

Investigating Matter (1600-1880)

Due to the combined efforts of several scientists throughout this time period, a model of what was eventually to be called the atom emerged. It began early in the 1600's when a man by the name of Robert Boyle challenged past ideas of the Greek philosophers who had suggested that all matter on Earth was

composed of one of the following four elements; earth, fire, water and air. Boyle expressed his belief that there were more than just four elements into which matter could be classified, although he was not specific about what they were.

In the same search for the most basic part of matter, a man named Antoine Lavoisier determined that if found, this would still be called an element. An element would be defined as a substance that cannot be further broken down by chemical means. To finally have a definition of what was really at the heart of their search was very instrumental in focusing scientists on their goals.

With this in mind, Allesandro Volta's voltaic cell (battery) became a popular way of chemically altering substances and experimenting with matter. Several scientists performed experiments where they passed electricity through substances. Today this process is known as electrolysis. In the electrolysis of water for example, when electricity is passed through water, the water splits up into hydrogen and oxygen gas. They observed that this would separate the substance into other components which could not be broken down further. They had finally isolated a part of matter that could not be further broken down – elements. It was observed that the initial substance always had different physical and chemical properties than did either of the resulting elements. Another very interesting observation was also made by a scientist named Joseph Proust when he actually quantified the elements that were being formed as the result of electrolysis and realized that they appeared in a pattern. Today this is known as the Law of Definite Proportions and it says that a compound is a pure substance that contains two or more elements in a fixed ratio.

Electrolysis of Water

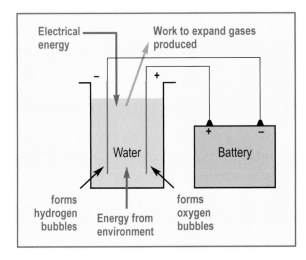

Dalton's Atomic Theory of Matter

In 1803, a man named John Dalton proposed an atomic theory. Remember that a theory is just an imaginative way to explain what is going on around us, it is not a law. The main ideas of his theory were as follows:

1. All matter is made up of very tiny things called atoms.

2. Atoms are the smallest building blocks of matter, and cannot be created or destroyed.

3. All atoms of the same element have the same mass and size, but they have a different mass and size from the atoms of other elements.

4. Compounds are created when atoms of different atoms join together in definite proportions.

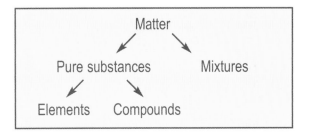

Based on this new theory by Dalton, an element is a pure substance made up of only one type of particle, or atom. Each element has its own distinct properties and cannot be broken down into simpler substances by means of a chemical change. We will refer to this model as the "bowling ball" model of the atom, where each atom is an indivisible sphere, like a small bowling ball. Unlike the Democritus model of the atom, there are different types and sizes of bowling balls!

"Bowling Ball"

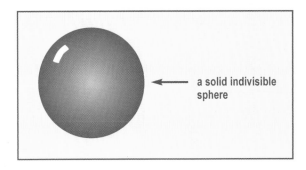

Subatomic Particles

With this new atomic model, scientists continued their search for more elements, only now with a greater confidence than ever. What made this research so difficult was that the atom is so small; it cannot be seen with the naked eye or even under a microscope. There was one type of experiment, however, that was particularly ground-breaking in further probing the structure of the atom.

Two Major Experiments

Gas Discharge Tube Experiment

Scientists, Volta and Proust, had already learned much about elements through electrolysis, but with help from two others, scientist Humphry Davy and expert glass blower Heinrich Geissler, a new and improved gas discharge tube was created, allowing scientists to examine the effect of electricity on gases under low pressures. The gas discharge tube consisted of a tightly sealed glass tube with a negatively charged end, called a cathode, and a positively charged end, called an anode. This new technology also had a very efficient pump with which the pressure inside the tube could be reduced significantly, allowing for the better transfer of electricity through the substance. (See diagram A on next page.)

It was observed that when electricity was turned on at the cathode, there was a mysterious green glow at the anode. The inference was that this must be the result of a sort of beam coming from the cathode and since it was moving towards the positive end, it must be negatively charged (opposite charges attract). Another interesting, and extremely crucial observation was that it did not matter what substance the cathode was made from (iron, silver, copper, etc.), the

beam always appeared and it was always green. The only logical explanation was that all elements must have one thing in common – a negatively charged particle.

Crookes' Corpuscle Experiment

In a similar experiment, a man named William Crookes conducted an experiment in a discharge tube with a small pinwheel inserted in between the cathode and anode. Upon passing an electric current between the ends he observed that the pinwheel actually began to spin as the beam of negatively charged particles ran from cathode to anode. This lead to the important discovery that cathode rays must have mass, and it was decided by many scientists that these tiny particles would be called electrons. (See diagram B.)

Two New Atomic Theories

J.J. Thompson

In the late 1800's, J.J. Thompson believed that since atoms were neutrally charged, they must also contain a positive portion to balance the charge of the negative electrons. Experiments were conducted and it was found that there was in fact a beam similar to that of the cathode, only positively charged and originating from the anode (travelling towards the cathode). Thompson called these particles protons. Here are some of the conclusions that Thompson made about the relationship between protons and electrons:

Once scientists had easy access to well-made pumps and discharge tubes, many began to investigate the movement of electricity through gases. This flow diagram summarizes what they learned.

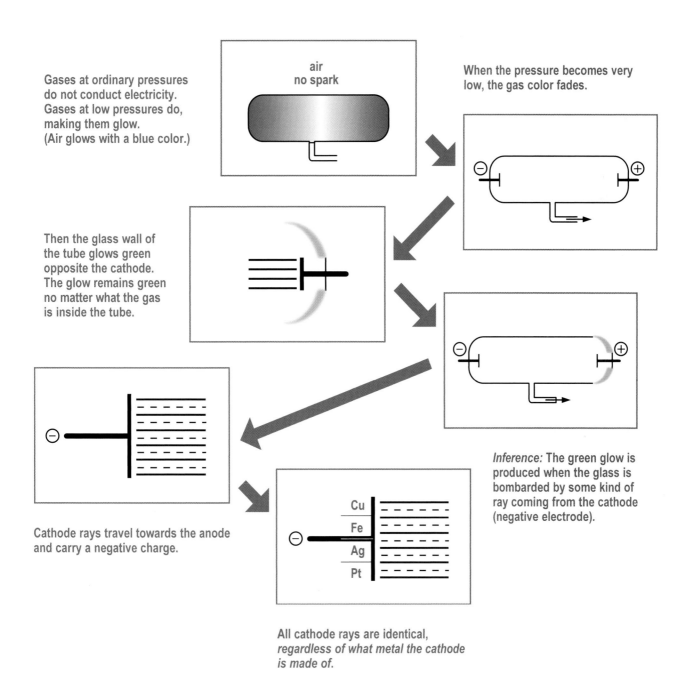

Gases at ordinary pressures do not conduct electricity. Gases at low pressures do, making them glow.
(Air glows with a blue color.)

air
no spark

When the pressure becomes very low, the gas color fades.

Then the glass wall of the tube glows green opposite the cathode. The glow remains green no matter what the gas is inside the tube.

Cathode rays travel towards the anode and carry a negative charge.

Cu
Fe
Ag
Pt

Inference: The green glow is produced when the glass is bombarded by some kind of ray coming from the cathode (negative electrode).

All cathode rays are identical, *regardless of what metal the cathode is made of.*

Atoms and Their Subatomic Particles | 171

In another experiment, Crookes mounted a tiny pinwheel inside a custom-made discharge tube. When the electric current was switched on, the pinwheel began to spin, much like a windmill in a strong breeze. To Crookes, this meant that the cathode rays must have mass as well a motion.Other scientists quickly accepted his idea that cathode rays are made of fast moving "corpuscles" — minute bits of matter. Just how tiny they are was investigated by the next great scientist to enter the story.

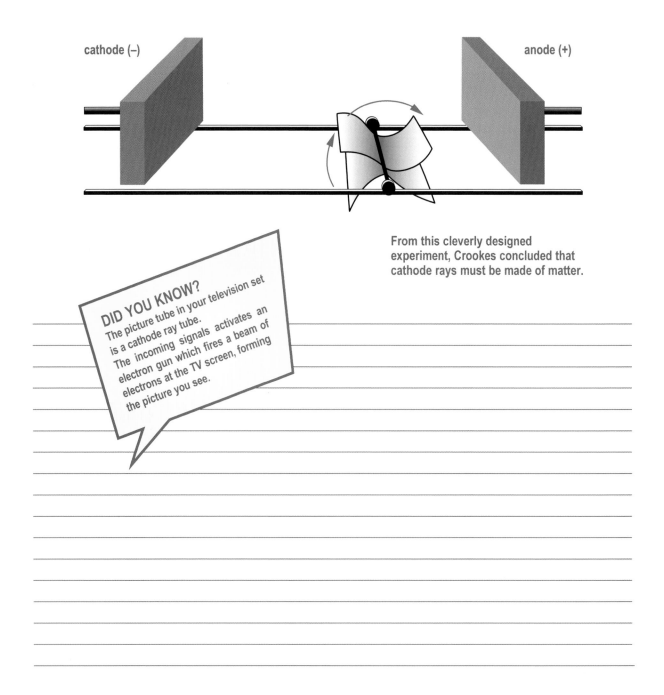

cathode (–)

anode (+)

From this cleverly designed experiment, Crookes concluded that cathode rays must be made of matter.

DID YOU KNOW?
The picture tube in your television set is a cathode ray tube. The incoming signals activates an electron gun which fires a beam of electrons at the TV screen, forming the picture you see.

1. All atoms contain positively charged particles called protons and negatively charged particles called electrons.

2. All protons from any type of atom are the same, and all electrons from any type of atom are the same.

3. Protons and electrons are very different from one another.

4. An electron and proton have the same amount of charge, but opposite.

5. A proton is much more massive than an electron.

Based on these five new ideas, Thompson's new model of the atom was compared to a "blueberry muffin", where the blueberries would be the electrons and the rest of the muffin dough would be the positive aspect of the atom.

"Blueberry Muffin"

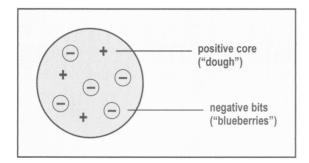

Bohr-Rutherford

In the early 1900's, scientist Ernest Rutherford performed an experiment which became very famous. He wanted to investigate gold atoms. He used radioactive alpha (positively charged) particles. Rutherford knew that when two positive or two negative particles came into close contact, they would repel each other, like when the North poles of two magnets are brought together. He sent a beam of alpha (+) particles through a very thin piece of gold foil, expecting to see that the alpha particles would travel straight through the foil to the other side. This did occur, however some of the particles also rebounded almost directly back off the foil. Rutherford reasoned that there must therefore be a dense positive portion of the atom that would cause this strong repelling reaction. Also, because most of the alpha particles did travel straight through, that there must be mostly empty space in an atom.

From these results, he proposed a model of the atom which became known as the "electron cloud" model. He explained that the atom actually looked like a tightly packed core of protons with a large, cloud of electrons surrounding it.

"Electron Cloud"

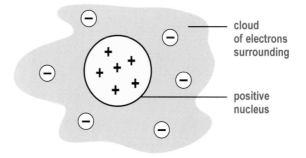

Some other puzzling questions arose, leading Rutherford and his student Niels Bohr to make some further deductions as to the contents of an atom. First of all, the relative mass of a gold atom was almost double that of the mass of the protons in that atom. Since electrons had almost no mass, Rutherford concluded that there must be other particles, likely neutral in charge in the core of the atom. He called them neutrons. These neutrons would be similar in mass to the proton, but with no charge.

Bohr could not understand why, if positive and negative charges attract, the electron cloud would not come spiralling into the center of the atom. He discovered the answer to this question by looking at the light spectrum of hydrogen more carefully. This later explained that, similar to the way planets of our solar system orbit the sun, the electrons of an atom orbit its positive nucleus. The reason the electrons are not attracted to the center is because of their various energy levels and the speed with which they literally orbit the nucleus. Electrons with more energy may jump to orbits further from the center. Based on these new discoveries, our most modern model of the atom is that of Bohr and Rutherford, and is based on the fact that there are different orbits or shells in which electrons can exist.

Rutherford-Bohr Model of the Atom

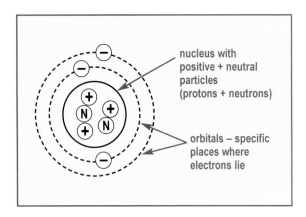

Lesson Summary

1. Once the scientific method was introduced and the idea that good science had to involve experimentation and physical evidence of concepts, the investigation of the structure of matter moved much more quickly.

2. Dalton's atomic theory stated that all matter is made of atoms, which cannot be created, destroyed or divided. He also defined an element as being made of one type of atom that cannot be further broken down.

3. Through many experiments involving electricity, it was discovered that atoms can actually be broken down into three smaller particles called subatomic particles; electrons, protons and neutrons.

Lesson #2 – Questions

1. What is the scientific method?

_____

_____

_____

_____

2. Outline the basic premise of Dalton's atomic theory.

_____

_____

_____

_____

3. Describe and draw the four main models of the atom in their chronological order.

_____

_____

_____

_____

4. What experiment proved J.J. Thompson's model wrong? Why?

_____

_____

_____

_____

Lesson #3 – Elements and the Periodic Table

Objectives:

- To be able to write names and symbols for the first 20 elements in the periodic table

- To distinguish between atomic mass and atomic number, and calculate the number of neutrons in an atom

- To outline the method that Mendeleev used to classify the elements and understand why his method was so powerful

- To describe the four main groupings of the periodic table and how their structure affects their reactivity

- To define the term isotope

Introduction

It is human nature to classify to make sense of things. It was no different just a couple of centuries ago when scientists began discovering elements. As the number of elements grew, so did the need to sort and classify them. Chemists all over the world, researching in different languages, *were working on discovering new elements, and so the first obstacle in the classification of the elements was finding a universal language with which to communicate.*

Symbols for the Elements

In order to solve the language problem, Jons Jakob Berzelius proposed a system of symbols to identify different elements. Each symbol for each element consists of one or two letters, the first as an upper case letter and the second (if present) as a lower case letter. The naming rules are as follows:

1. The first letter is always the first letter of the name of the element. For example: H = hydrogen, O = oxygen, B = boron.

2. A second letter is added to the symbol if the first letter of the element has already been used, and it is the second letter in the name of the element. For example: He = Helium (H was already used for hydrogen), Be = Beryllium (B was already used for Boron).

3. If the second letter in the name of the element has already been used, take the next available letter. For example: Bk = Berkelium (Be and Br have already been used).

4. There are seven metals that were known to the ancients by their Latin names, hence their symbols are derived from these names. They are: Ag = Silver (argentum), Au = gold (aurum), Cu = copper (cuprum), Fe = iron (ferrum), Hg = mercury (hydrargyrum), Pb = lead (plumbum) and Sn = tin (stannum).

Although each language has its own way of pronouncing and spelling each element name, everyone uses these universal symbols based on the English alphabet, not its own.

Classification of the Elements

Before arriving at the classification system that we are familiar with today, there were some valuable attempts at sorting the elements. An obvious method of classifying the elements was based on their ability to conduct electricity. Based on the frequency with which all scientists relied upon Volta's invention of the battery to conduct their experiments, they became very familiar with which elements were better conductors than others. This led them to a means of classifying elements still used today; metals (conduct electricity very well), non-metals (do not conduct electricity) and metalloids (conduct electricity somewhat). Although not wrong, scientists wished for a means of classifying elements based on more than one characteristic.

 In 1869, with the help of Dalton's notion of "relative mass", a Russian scientist named Dmitri Mendeleev, arranged all known elements in increasing order of their masses. Once he had done this, he looked for trends and similarities among the properties of the elements. He discovered that every eighth element had similar, repeating properties. He arranged the elements in a table so that ones which possessed similar properties were placed under each other. He called this the periodic table, because of its repeating nature. In fact, Mendeleev was so confident that he was correct in his findings; he used his table to predict the existence of elements that had not yet been discovered. He did this by leaving empty spaces in his table where he could not place an element because of its properties. This became a very powerful tool in classifying elements, and many elements that he predicted would exist, were in fact discovered as a result of this amazing table.

This is the type of information that Mendeleev wrote on his property cards.

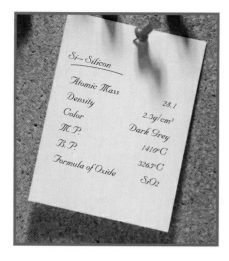

In 1915, it was discovered that as the relative mass of the elements increased, so did the number of protons in each atom's nucleus, the atomic number. Mendeleev's periodic table was reorganized slightly according to atomic number as opposed to atomic mass. The changes were relatively few and did account for some of the troubles that Mendeleev had encountered. (See the *Modern Day Periodic Table* on the next page.)

Atomic Number, Atomic Mass and Atomic Structure

The atomic number of an element tells us about the structure of the atom. It indicates the number of protons present in the nucleus, and based on our model of the atom, it possesses the same number of electrons as protons. For example, the atomic number of oxygen is 8. This means that an oxygen atom has 8 protons and 8 electrons.

An atom also contains neutrons; however the atomic number does not provide us with any information about the number of neutrons present. In order to calculate this, we require another number called the mass number. The mass number represents the total number of protons and neutrons in each atom. To calculate the number of neutrons in an atom of oxygen, subtract the atomic number from the mass number. In our example, the mass number of oxygen is 16. Subtract 8 from 16 to get 8. Therefore, there are 8 neutrons.

Oxygen Atom's Structure

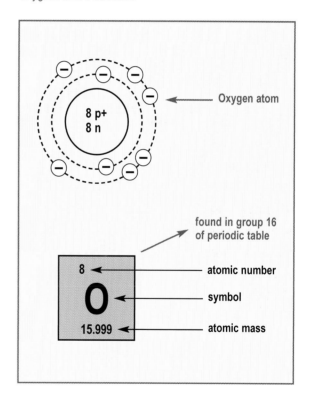

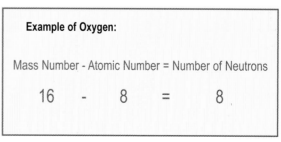

	1 IA																	18 0
1	1 **H** hydrogen 1.0	2 IIA											13 IIIA	14 IVA	15 VA	16 VIA	17 VIIA	2 **He** helium 4.0
2	3 **Li** lithium 6.9	4 **Be** beryllium 9.0											5 **B** boron 10.8	6 **C** carbon 12.0	7 **N** nitrogen 14.0	8 **O** oxygen 16.0	9 **F** fluorine 19.0	10 **Ne** neon 20.2
3	11 **Na** sodium 23.0	12 **Mg** magnesium 24.3	3 IIIB	4 IVB	5 VB	6 VIB	7 VIIB	8 ——	9 VII	10 ——	11 IB	12 IIB	13 **Al** aluminum 27.0	14 **Si** silicon 28.1	15 **P** phosphorus 31.0	16 **S** sulfur 32.1	17 **Cl** chlorine 35.5	18 **Ar** argon 39.9
4	19 **K** potassium 39.1	20 **Ca** calcium 40.1	21 **Sc** scandium 45.0	22 **Ti** titanium 47.9	23 **V** vanadium 50.9	24 **Cr** chromium 52.0	25 **Mn** manganese 54.9	26 **Fe** iron 55.9	27 **Co** cobalt 58.9	28 **Ni** nickel 58.7	29 **Cu** copper 63.5	30 **Zn** zinc 65.4	31 **Ga** gallium 69.7	32 **Ge** germanium 72.6	33 **As** arsenic 74.9	34 **Se** selenium 79.0	35 **Br** bromine 79.9	36 **Kr** krypton 83.8
5	37 **Rb** rubidium 85.5	38 **Sr** strontium 87.6	39 **Y** yttrium 88.9	40 **Zr** zirconium 91.2	41 **Nb** niobium 92.9	42 **Mo** molybdenum 95.9	43 **Tc** technetium 98	44 **Ru** ruthenium 101.1	45 **Rh** rhodium 102.9	46 **Pd** palladium 106.4	47 **Ag** silver 107.9	48 **Cd** cadmium 112.4	49 **In** indium 114.8	50 **Sn** tin 118.7	51 **Sb** antimony 121.8	52 **Te** tellurium 127.6	53 **I** iodine 126.9	54 **Xe** xenon 131.3
6	55 **Cs** cesium 140.0	56 **Ba** barium 137.3	57 ***La** lanthanum 138.9	72 **Hf** hafnium 178.5	73 **Ta** tantalum 181.0	74 **W** tungsten 183.8	75 **Re** rhenium 186.2	76 **Os** osmium 190.2	77 **Ir** iridium 192.2	78 **Pt** platinum 195.1	79 **Au** gold 197.0	80 **Hg** mercury 200.6	81 **Tl** thallium 204.4	82 **Pb** lead 207.2	83 **Bi** bismuth 209.0	84 **Po** polonium (210)	85 **At** astatine (210)	86 **Rn** radon (222)
7	87 **Fr** francium (223)	88 **Ra** radium (226)	89 **+Ac** actinium (227)	104 **Rf** rutherfordium (261)	105 **Db** dubnium (262)	106 **Sg** seaborgium (266)	107 **Bh** borium (264)	108 **Hs** hassium (269)	109 **Mt** meitnerium (268)	110 **Uun** ununnilium (269)	111 **Uuu** unununium (272)	112 **Uub** ununbium (277)	113 **Uut** ununtrium					

* Lanthanide Series	58 **Ce** cerium 140.1	59 **Pr** praseodymium 140.9	60 **Nd** neodymium 144.2	61 **Pm** promethium 144.9	62 **Sm** samarium 150.4	63 **Eu** europium 152.0	64 **Gd** gadolinium 157.3	65 **Tb** terbium 158.9	66 **Dy** dysprosium 162.5	67 **Ho** holmium 164.9	68 **Er** erbium 167.3	69 **Tm** thulium 168.9	70 **Yb** ytterbium 173.0	71 **Lu** lutetium 175.0
+ Actinide Series	90 **Th** thorium 232.0	91 **Pa** protactinium 231.0	92 **U** uranium 238.0	93 **Np** neptunium (237)	94 **Pu** plutonium (244)	95 **Am** americium (243)	96 **Cm** curium (247)	97 **Bk** berkelium (247)	98 **Cf** californium (251)	99 **Es** einsteinium (252)	100 **Fm** fermium (257)	101 **Md** mendelevium (258)	102 **No** nobelium (259)	103 **Lr** lawrencium (262)

Families of Elements

Each element in the periodic table has distinctive properties.
When elements have similar properties they are grouped into families.

- *Alkali Metals*
- *Alkali Earth Metals*
- *Transition Metals*
- *Rare Earth Metals*
- *Other Metals*
- *Nonmetals*
- *Halogens*
- *Noble Gases*
- *Metalloids*

Both the atomic number and the mass number appear on the periodic table, for each element. It is important to understand that the mass number is not expressed in normal units of mass such as the kilogram or gram. It is expressed in atomic mass units (u) which show each elements relative mass to the lightest element, hydrogen. For instance, chlorine's mass number is 35 (actually 34.99). This means that its mass is 35 times that of hydrogen. The mass of a proton and a neutron is each 1 u, while the mass of an electron is 1/2000 u. The mass due to electrons is usually considered nothing when using mass number, because it is so small.

The reason that some mass numbers on the periodic table are not even numbers is due to the existence of isotopes. Isotopes are elements with the same atomic number (same number of protons) but different mass numbers (different number of neutrons). This difference means that they have different physical properties, perhaps color, or boiling point, but have the same chemical properties, such as how they bond with other elements.

For instance, lithium is an element that has isotopes. All lithium atoms contain 3 protons since lithium's atomic number is 3. However, some lithium atoms have mass number 6 (contain 3 neutrons) and some 7 (contain 4 neutrons). The mass number given for lithium on the periodic table is 6.941, a weighted average. This means that many, many more lithium atoms containing 4 neutrons are present in nature because the mass number is closer to 7.

Lithium Isotopes

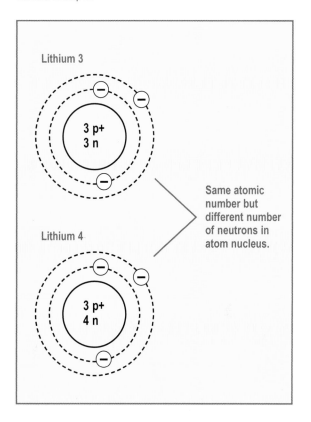

Same atomic number but different number of neutrons in atom nucleus.

Groups of the Periodic Table

The modern periodic table, much like Mendeleev's, was arranged in vertical columns and horizontal rows. The horizontal rows are called periods and a period generally contains eight elements, not having many common properties. The vertical columns are often referred to as groups or families and have similar properties and strong relationships with each other.

The electron configuration of an atom is the main factor in determining which groups will have similar properties. Just like a school bus can only hold a certain number of kids, electron orbitals also have a maximum capacity. When the outside orbital is full, it means that the atom is stable, and does not react well with other atoms. However, when the outer orbital is not full, atoms react with one another, and they always react in such a way that their outer orbitals become full, and they become stable. Atoms with the same number of electrons in their outer orbitals are placed in groups because they have the same level of reactivity. Some of these groups have been given special names:

Group 1 is known as the *Alkali Metals*. This group of elements contains hydrogen (H), lithium (Li), sodium (Na), and potassium (K), among others. These metals react quickly and drastically upon exposure to air. The highly reactive nature of this group is due to each element's electron configuration. They each contain only one electron in the outer shell, leading to an unstable and reactive group of elements. As the size of the atom increases (increasing atomic number) so does the reactivity. ◼

Group 2 is called the *Alkaline Earth Metals*. The elements in this group are: beryllium (Be), magnesium (Mg), and calcium (Ca), among others. This family of elements is fairly reactive, but not as much as group 1. Each atom in this group has two electrons in its outer shell. This structure makes it slightly more stable than the alkali metals, but still reactive. Again, the larger atoms are more reactive than the smaller ones. ◻

Group 17 is named the *Halogens* and contains elements such as: fluorine (F), chlorine (Cl), bromine (Br) and iodine (I), among others. These elements are highly reactive and are all non-metals. The outer electron shells of these atoms are missing one electron, making them unstable. Unlike the metals, the element with the smallest atoms, fluorine, is most reactive. ◻

Group 18 is the *Noble Gases* and contains all gaseous elements such as: helium (He), Neon (Ne), argon (Ar) and krypton (Kr), among others. These elements are considered non-reactive elements because they have a full outer shell of electrons making their atomic structure very stable. ◻

_____
_____
_____
_____
_____
_____
_____
_____
_____
_____
_____
_____
_____
_____
_____
_____
_____
_____

Lesson Summary

1. Universal symbols were created for each element to avoid confusion between different countries and languages. The symbols consist of one or two letters from the English alphabet.

2. Mendeleev noticed that when the elements were placed in order of increasing atomic mass, every eighth element had similar, repeating properties. This lead to the very first periodic table of elements.

3. The modern day periodic table is very similar to Mendeleev's, but is ordered according to increasing atomic number.

4. Atomic number is the number of protons in an atom, while mass number is measured in relative mass units, and represents the total number of protons and neutrons.

5. Isotopes are atoms of the same element that contain the same number of protons, but different number of neutrons.

6. Groups of elements in the periodic table have very similar properties, based on the electron configuration of their atoms.

Lesson #3 – Questions

1. Why was it so important to have a universal naming system for the elements?

_____

_____

_____

_____

_____

2. How was the periodic table such a powerful tool in the past?

_____

_____

_____

_____

_____

3. In a chart, list the group names, group numbers, and main properties of four groups in the periodic table.

_____

_____

_____

_____

_____

4. How many protons, electrons and neutrons do each of the following atoms have? What are their chemical symbols?

(a) aluminum _____

(b) titanium _____

(c) fluorine _____

(d) xenon _____

Lesson #4 – Bonding Atoms to Form Compounds

Objectives:

- To define the term compound in terms of the law of definite proportions

- To explain the difference between ionic and molecular bonding of atoms and to provide examples

- To determine whether an ion will be positive or negative based on atomic structure

- To understand the relationship between valence electrons and reactivity of a compound

Introduction

As mentioned in the last lesson, some elements are far more reactive than others due to the configuration of their outer orbit, or shell, of electrons. Atoms are always looking to be as stable as possible, and this requires having a full outer shell of electrons. Atoms in the alkali metals group, such as potassium, need to get rid of an electron to become stable. Atoms in the halogens group, such as chlorine, need to obtain an electron to become stable. Do you see how potassium and chlorine could be the solution to one another's need to become stable? A chemical bond is formed when atoms donate or share electrons with each other, and this is how compounds are formed.

Compounds

The law of definite proportions states that a compound is a pure substance formed when two or more atoms bond together in a fixed proportion. The new substance formed has different properties than the atoms that formed it. For example, when hydrogen and oxygen atoms bond, there are various possible outcomes. If 2 hydrogen atoms bond with 1 oxygen atom, the result is water (H_2O), but if 2 hydrogen atoms bond with 2 oxygen atoms, the result is a new substance called hydrogen peroxide (H_2O_2). Water and hydrogen peroxide, although made of the same two elements, are very different substances because of the ratio of hydrogen to oxygen atoms. Hydrogen peroxide acts to kill bacteria, while water does not.

water

hydrogen peroxide

Difference in Structures

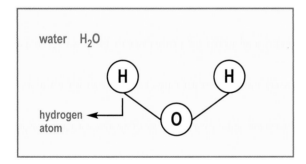

water H_2O

hydrogen atom ⟵

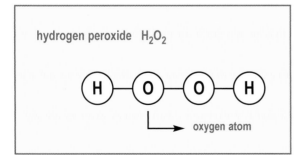

hydrogen peroxide H_2O_2

oxygen atom ⟶

There are two types of bonding; ionic and covalent. Ionic bonding is the result of one atom donating one or more electrons to another atom. Covalent bonding, on the other hand, is the sharing of electrons between two atoms. Both types of bonding make each atom more stable and build compounds. The only electrons that are affected in chemical bonding are the outer shell electrons because they are loosely bound. These are often referred to as valence electrons. It is an atoms valence that will determine in which ratio it will bond with another atom.

Ionic Bonding

In order for an ionic bond to be formed, electrons are actually exchanged, meaning that one atom loses an electron, while the other atom gains an electron. Atoms are neutral because they contain the same number of protons as electrons. When an electron is lost by an atom, it becomes slightly positive and when an electron is gained by an atom, the atom becomes slightly negative. A charged atom is called an ion, either positive or negative. As a result of this exchange of electrons, an attractive force between the positive and negative ions occurs, forming an ionic compound. Ionic bonds are formed between metals (give electrons) and non-metals (take electrons). (See the first diagram on top of page 187.) ⤢

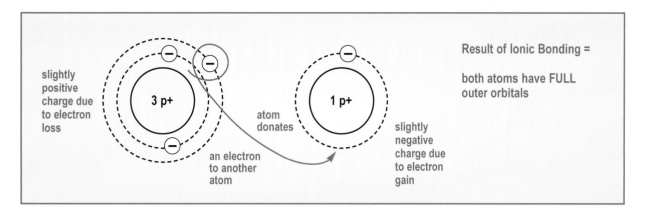

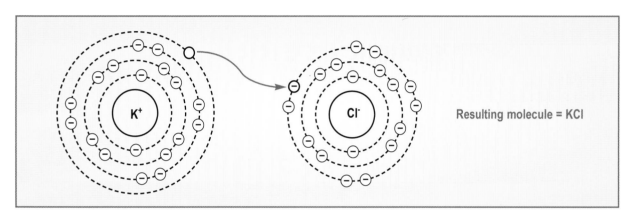

For instance, let's use our previous example of potassium (a Group 1 alkali metal) and chlorine (a Group 17 halogen) to demonstrate the principles of ionic bonding. The second diagram above shows the atomic structures of a potassium atom and a chlorine atom.

Potassium has 1 valence electron. Chlorine has 7 valence electrons. An ionic bond forms between these two atoms when potassium donates an electron to chlorine. Potassium is now a positive ion (+1) and chlorine is a negative ion (-1). Due to their opposite charges, they are attracted to one another to form an ionic compound called potassium chloride (KCl). This is an example of one to one bonding, meaning that one atom of an element bonds with one atom of another type of element, and only occurs with halogens and alkali metals.

A Group 2 alkaline earth metal, such as magnesium, can also form an ionic bond with chlorine. Magnesium has 2 valence electrons, which it must get rid of to form a stable outer shell. A chlorine atom only requires 1 electron, but 2 chlorine atoms require 2 electrons. Magnesium donates 1 electron to each chlorine atom, making itself a positive ion (+2) and making each of the chlorine atoms negative ions (-1).

Elements Group	1	2	13	14	15	16	17	18
Type of Ion	+	+	+	+	–	–	–	n/a
# Valence e⁻	1	2	3	4	5	6	7	8 (full)
Valency (# bonds formed)	1	2	3	4	3	2	1	0

The magnesium atom is attracted to the chlorine to form an ionic compound called magnesium chloride ($MgCl_2$). This is an example of two to one bonding, meaning that one atom of an element bonds with 2 atoms of another element. Other ionic compounds of different ratios can occur; it depends strictly on an atoms valency.

Ionic bonds are strong and because the attractive force between ions (the ionic bonds) is the same in all directions, substances with crystal lattices are formed. The bonds extend from one ion to the next throughout the entire solid, and attractive forces between molecules are very strong.

Crystal Lattice Formed in Ionic Bonding

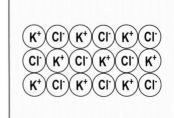

Each KCl molecule has a ⊕ and a ⊖ end, which causes more KCl's to be attracted, forming a rigid, organized structure called a lattice.

Covalent Bonding

A covalent, or molecular, bond is formed when two or more atoms share their electrons. Molecular compounds, unlike ionic compounds are composed of uncharged (neutral) atoms. Because atoms are physically sharing electrons to become more stable, molecular bonds between atoms are extremely strong, however the bonds between molecules are fairly weak.

For example, water is a molecular compound because hydrogen and oxygen actually share electrons to fill their outer shells.

Sharing Electrons

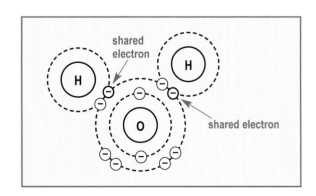

The primary differences between ionic and molecular bonding can be summarized in the following table.

Summary Table Between Ionic and Molecular Bonding

Type of Bond	Electrons	Strength of Bond Between:	
		Atoms	Molecules
Ionic	exchanged	strong	very strong
Molecular	shared	strong	weaker

Formula Writing

As mentioned earlier, the number of valence electrons an atom has will determine how it will bond with other atoms. Valence is the number of bonds an atom can form. The first shell around the nucleus of an atom can hold a maximum of two electrons, while both the second and third shells can hold a maximum of eight electrons (sometimes referred to as an octet). Let's examine how the periodic table of the elements can be used to determine the valency of an atom for the first twenty elements.

Elements in group 1 have one valence electron, which can be donated to another atom to form a single bond. For instance, hydrogen and sodium can only form one bond. Elements in group 2 have two valence electrons, which can be donated to another atom to form two bonds. For example, beryllium and magnesium can both form two bonds.

Outer Orbitals of Group 1 & Group 2 Elements

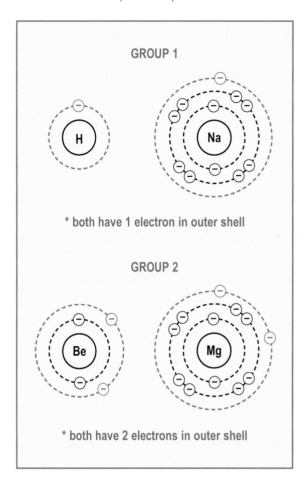

After beryllium is boron, in group 13. Boron and aluminum have three valence electrons, and therefore can form three bonds. Group 14 elements, such as carbon and silicon, can form four bonds with other atoms because they have four valence electrons. Four is the maximum number of bonds that can be formed by the first twenty elements. (See diagram.)

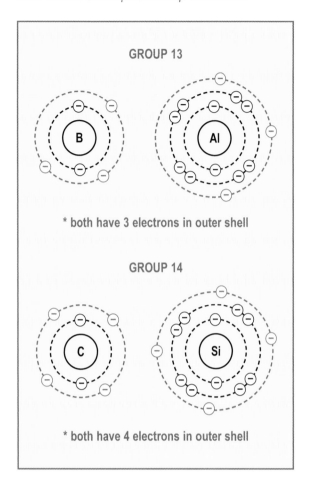

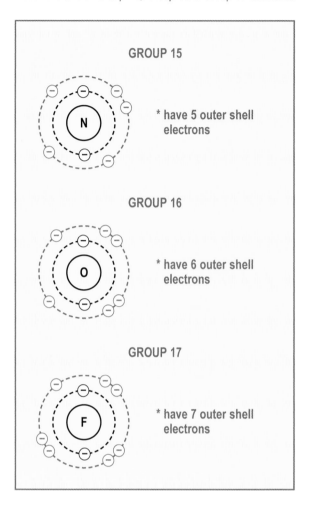

At this point in the periodic table, the number of bonds an element forms begins to drop as the group number increases. Group 15 elements, such as nitrogen and phosphorous, have five valence electrons and are looking for three electrons to form an octet. They can form three bonds. Group 16 elements, such as oxygen and sulphur can form two bonds, and Group 17 elements, such as fluorine and chlorine, can form only one bond.

Because elements such as helium, neon and argon all have full outer shells, these elements do not form bonds with other atoms easily.

Outer Orbitals of Group 18 Elements

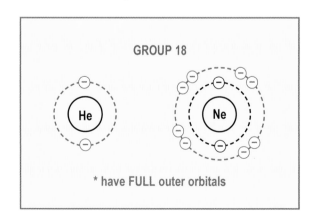

Now that we know the valence numbers for the first twenty elements, we can use this information to write formulas for various molecules. A molecular formula tells us three things about a particular molecule; what type of atoms make up the molecule, the number of each type of atom, and the total number of atoms in each molecule. When writing formulas, we use the element symbols to represent the type of atom, and we use subscript number to indicate the number of molecules of each type of atom. If there is only one atom of an element, no number is written (the number one is assumed).

In order to determine the formula of a compound, there are three steps to follow. Let's follow these steps to determine the molecular formula for the compound calcium fluoride.

1. Determine the valence (number of bonds that can be formed) of each element.
calcium = 2, fluorine = 1

2. Switch the valence numbers to the opposite element.
calcium (1), fluorine (2)

3. Write the formula, using the valence numbers as subscripts for each element.
CaF_2

Let's try potassium bromide.

1. potassium = 1, bromine = 1

2. potassium (1), bromine (1)

3. KBr

Let's try aluminum oxide.

1. aluminum = 3, oxygen = 2

2. aluminum (2), oxygen (3)

3. Al_2O_3

Table of Formulas
E.g.

Formula	# Elements	# of Each Element	Total # Atoms	Others:
CaF_2	2	1 Ca atom 2 Fluorine atoms	3	• H_2SO_4
KBr	2	1 K atom 1 Br atom	2	• $C_6H_{12}O_6$
Al_2O_3	2	2 Al atoms 3 O atoms	5	• Cl_2

Lesson Summary

1. The law of definite proportions states that a compound is a pure substance formed when two or more atoms bond together in a fixed proportion.

2. Ionic bonds occur when the <u>exchange</u> of electrons occurs between two atoms. The exchange of electrons creates ions which are charged atoms, and the bond is formed by the attraction of positive and negative ions.

3. Covalent or molecular bonds are formed when atoms <u>share</u> electrons in order to fill their outer shells.

4. Valence electrons are the electrons found in the outer shell. The first shell has the capacity to hold two electrons, while the second and third shells can both hold a maximum of eight electrons.

5. Valence is the number of bonds that an atom can form.

6. <u>Molecular formulas</u> indicate the elements present in the compound, the number of each type of atom, and the total number of atoms.

7. Valences are used to write the molecular formula of a compound.

Lesson #4 – Questions

1. What is a valence electron? How and why does the number of valence electrons affect the reactivity of an element and the number of bonds an atom can form?

_____
_____
_____
_____
_____

2. Compare and provide examples for ionic and molecular bonds.

_____
_____
_____
_____
_____

3. How many total atoms are in each of the following formulas?

(a) $6H_2O$ _____

(b) $3NaCl$ _____

(c) H_2SO_4 _____

(d) $2C_6H_{12}O_6$ _____

4. What does the law of definite proportions mean?

_____
_____
_____
_____
_____

Simple Chemical Reactions

Lesson #5 – Balancing Equations

Objectives:

- To distinguish between physical and chemical properties of a substance

- To become familiar with the terms and symbols used in writing chemical equations

- To explain the laws of conservation of mass and energy and how they relate to the balancing of chemical equations

- To balance a chemical equation, given an unbalanced equation

- To recognize the four basic types of chemical reactions

Introduction

Before introducing the topic of chemical reactions, it is important to remember a few terms that were discussed in the opening lesson. Recall that a physical change is when a substance undergoes changes that do not involve the creation of a new substance. This is often called a change of physical state. The example that we used was the freezing of water to form ice.

Chemical changes involve the creation of a brand new substance. We can detect a chemical change in one or more ways; a temperature change, a color change, or a gas is produced, etc. Whether a reaction produces a physical or a chemical change, it can always be written as an equation where the starting substance is on one side and the resulting substance is on the other side. But, just like math class, an equation means that both sides must be equal. This lesson will focus on writing proper equations and balancing them.

Physical and Chemical Properties

Physical properties of substances can be observed without a change in substance. Properties such as color, odor, density, boiling and melting points are all physical properties. Chemical properties, on the other hand, can only be observed when a change in substance occurs, such as how iron reacts with oxygen to form rust, or how chlorine gas reacts violently with sodium. In order to better understand the difference between physical and chemical properties, it is useful to compare the two to human qualities. Physical properties are like the physical appearance of humans; hair and eye color, height, skin color, and blood type. Chemical properties are much like the personality traits of humans and how they react in different situations; jealous, mean, friendly or generous. The chemical and physical properties of various substances are useful in predicting how different substances will react with one another in a chemical reaction, and help in writing chemical equations for reactions.

Writing Chemical Equations

In order to examine chemical reactions more closely, we must be comfortable expressing the reaction as a scientific or chemical equation. To write a chemical equation, we must first become familiar with some of the terms and symbols used.

Just like a mathematical equation, chemical equations have two equal sides, the left and the right. The left side of the equation represents the substances that react with one another – the reactants. The right side of the equation represents the substances that result from the reaction – the products.

Unlike math, an equals sign "=" is not used to separate the two sides, instead an arrow is used, indicating that the reactants become the products. If more than one substance is reacting, then the two substances (or more) are separated by a plus sign "+". The same applies on the right side with the products.

Human Personality vs Properties of Matter

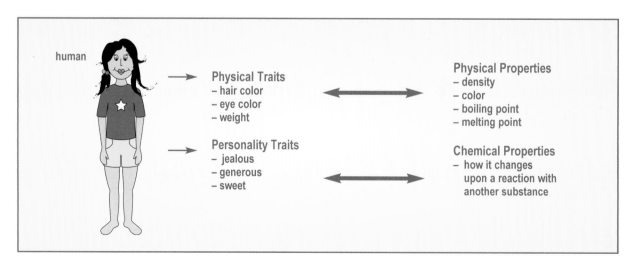

Some other signs that are commonly found in chemical equations are the symbols indicating the physical state of a compound or an element. These symbols occur after the chemical formula of the substance; (s) = solid, (l) = liquid, (g) = gas, and (aq) = aqueous solution (meaning dissolved in water).

Lastly, there are numbers in the equation called co-efficients, and they are found in front of each formula, indicating the number of molecules of that particular substance that are used or produced in the reaction. It is important to note that co-efficients are not an indicator of how many atoms are present. Multiply the co-efficient by the number of atoms in one molecule to get the total number of atoms of each type.

For example:

1. $5 H_2O$ = 5 water molecules, but $5 \times H_2$ = 10 hydrogen atoms, and $5 \times O$ = 5 oxygen atoms.

2. $2 Al_2O_3$ = 2 aluminum oxide molecules, but $2 \times Al_2$ = 4 aluminum atoms, and $2 \times O_3$ = 6 oxygen atoms.

Chemical Formula

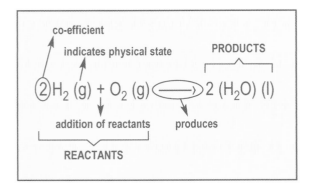

Laws of Conservation

Recall that energy is the ability to do work. The law of conservation of energy states that energy can neither be created nor destroyed but may be transformed from one form to another. For instance, when you fill up a car with gas, the chemical bonds holding the molecules of gasoline together have potential energy (the ability to do work). Inside your car, that potential energy is converted to electrical and mechanical energy to make the car move. Any energy that is not used to make the car move is wasted energy and generally expelled as thermal energy or heat. No energy has been created or destroyed, simply changed from one form to the next.

Similarly, the law of conservation of mass states that mass can neither be created nor destroyed, and the total mass of the substances involved in a reaction remains constant. Take for example the chemical reaction of hydrogen and oxygen to form water. If 4 mg of hydrogen are completely combined with 32 mg of oxygen, the resulting water must have a mass of 36 mg. In other words, the mass of the reactants (left side) is equal to the mass of the products (right side). Mass was not created or destroyed in this reaction.

Word Equation

Hydrogen + Oxygen ⟶ Water
4mg   32mg   36mg

Balancing Chemical Equations

Given the law of conservation of mass, we now know that the mass of the reactants must equal the mass of the products. We also learned previously that each atom has a particular mass, called the atomic mass. If mass must be conserved and each atom has a specific mass, that must mean that the number of atoms in a reaction must also be conserved.

Let's examine the following word equation that was discussed earlier.

$$H_2 \text{ (g)} + O_2 \text{ (g)} \longrightarrow H_2O \text{ (l)}$$

If we count the number of oxygen molecules on each side, we get 2 on the left, and 1 on the right. If we count the number of hydrogen molecules on each side, we get 2 on the left, and 2 on the right. The hydrogen atoms are balanced, but the oxygen atoms are not balanced. To correct for this, add a co-efficient of 2 in front of the water molecule. Recall that a co-efficient represents the number of molecules, NOT the number of atoms.

Two water molecules contain 4 hydrogen and 2 oxygen atoms.

$$H_2 \text{ (g)} + O_2 \text{ (g)} \longrightarrow 2 H_2O \text{ (l)}$$

Is the equation balanced now? No, the hydrogen atoms are unbalanced now, so we must add a co-efficient of 2 in front of the reactant hydrogen. Now the equation has 4 hydrogen atoms and 2 oxygen atoms on each side. Now the equation is balanced.

$$2 H_2 \text{ (g)} + O_2 \text{ (g)} \longrightarrow 2 H_2O \text{ (l)}$$

Here are some basic guidelines that will help you balance more complex chemical equations, but remember every equation is different and there are no hard-fast rules. It depends on the situation. As we go through the process of balancing an equation, let's use the following as our example:

$$C_3H_8 + O_2 \longrightarrow CO_2 + H_2O$$

1. Ensure that the chemical formulas for each compound are written correctly. Double check the periodic table for valencies.

2. The first element that you choose to balance should be the one from the compound containing the most atoms and that is present in the largest amount. DO NOT select hydrogen or oxygen. Balance this element by placing a co-efficient in front of the appropriate chemical formula.

In this example, C_3H_8 is the compound that contains the most atoms, and the element we choose to balance is carbon. There are 3 carbon atoms on the left, so place the co-efficient 3 in front of the CO_2 molecule on the right. Now carbon is balanced.

$$C_3H_8 + O_2 \longrightarrow 3\ CO_2 + H_2O$$

3. Balance any remaining elements that are not hydrogen or oxygen. This may involve switching the co-efficient from step 2.

In this example, there are no other elements, except for hydrogen and oxygen.

4. Balance the hydrogen and oxygen atoms.

In this example, there are 8 hydrogen atoms on the left, so place the co-efficient 4 in front of H_2O. Now hydrogen is balanced. There are 10 oxygen atoms on the right, so place the co-efficient 5 in front of O_2. Now oxygen is balanced.

$$C_3H_8 + 5\ O_2 \longrightarrow 3\ CO_2 + 4\ H_2O$$

5. Check that all co-efficients are whole numbers and that they are reduced to the lowest possible ratios.

6. Double check that the equation is balanced on the reactants and products side. Putting a check mark above elements that are balanced helps.

Let's try an example.

$$Fe\ (s) + HCl\ (aq) \longrightarrow FeCl_2\ (aq) + H_2\ (g)$$
(unbalanced)

Balance the Cl atoms by adding a 2 in front of HCl.

$$Fe\ (s) + 2\ HCl\ (aq) \longrightarrow FeCl_2\ (aq) + H_2\ (g)$$

This equation is now balanced as nothing was required to balance the Fe and H atoms.

Let's try one more example.

$$Mg\ (s) + O_2\ (g) \longrightarrow MgO\ (s)\ \text{(unbalanced)}$$

Balance Mg atoms. Already balanced.

Balance O atoms by placing a 2 in front of MgO.

$$Mg\ (s) + O_2\ (g) \longrightarrow 2\ MgO\ (s)$$
(unbalanced)

Check equation, find Mg unbalanced. Balance Mg by placing a 2 in front of Mg.

$$2\ Mg\ (s) + O_2\ (g) \longrightarrow 2\ MgO\ (s)$$

Types of Chemical Reactions

Balancing equations is useful if you are given the unbalanced reaction equation, as in the above example. However, in real-life chemistry, you will not always be given the equation. Chemists need a way to predict how two or more substances will react with one another in order to get the chemical equation. As mentioned already in this lesson, knowing the physical and chemical properties of some compounds is useful in helping predict what type of reaction might occur, but being able to recognize certain types of reactions is also useful. There are four basic types of reactions that can occur.

1. Combination or Synthesis reactions

- This occurs when two or more elements react to form a compound

- The general formula for this is:
$$A + Z \longrightarrow AZ$$

- For example, sodium reacts with chlorine gas to form sodium chloride: $2\ Na\ (s) + Cl_2\ (g) \longrightarrow 2\ NaCl\ (s)$

2. Decomposition reactions

- This occurs when one compound is broken down (usually by heat) to form two or more elements

- The general formula for this is:
$$AZ \longrightarrow A + Z$$

- For example, mercury (II) oxide decomposes to produce mercury and oxygen gas:
$2\ HgO\ (s) \longrightarrow 2\ Hg\ (l) + O_2\ (g)$

3. Single Replacement reactions

- This occurs when an element and a compound react and the element replaces another element in the compound. (Imagine a person cutting in on a couple dancing, and replacing one of them.)

- The general formula for this is:
$$A + BZ \longrightarrow B + AZ$$

- For example, zinc reacts with copper (II) sulphate to produce zinc sulphate and copper: $Zn\ (s) + CuSO_4\ (aq) \longrightarrow ZnSO_4\ (aq) + Cu\ (s)$

4. Double Displacement reactions

- This occurs when two compounds react so that they switch a positive ion for a positive ion. (Imagine two dancing couples exchanging partners)

- The general formula for this is:
$$AX + BZ \longrightarrow AZ + BX$$

- For example, silver nitrate reacts with hydrochloric acid to produce nitric acid and silver chloride:
$AgNO_3\ (aq) + HCl\ (aq) \longrightarrow HNO_3\ (aq) + AgCl\ (s)$

Lesson Summary

1. Density, boiling and melting points, color and odor are physical properties of chemical substances and can be compared to a person's physical appearance traits.

2. How a substance reacts with another substance is a chemical property and can be compared to a person's personality traits.

3. Chemical equations are very much like mathematical equations in that both sides of the equation must be equal.
The left side holds the reactants, while the right side holds the products of a chemical reaction.

4. The laws of conservation of mass and energy state that neither mass nor energy can be created or destroyed.

5. A chemical equation must have the same number of atoms on each side. In order to accomplish this, we place numbers called co-efficients in front of certain compounds or elements to balance the equation.

6. The four basic types of chemical reactions are: composition (or synthesis), decomposition, single replacement and double displacement.

Lesson #5 – Questions

1. What are the two laws of conservation?

_____

_____

_____

_____

_____

2. Name and give the general equations for the four types of chemical reactions.

_____

_____

_____

_____

_____

3. Balance the following equations.

(a) $Fe(s) + HCl(aq) \longrightarrow FeCl_2(aq) + H_2(g)$

_____

_____

_____

_____

_____

(b) $C_4H_{10}(g) + O_2(g) \longrightarrow CO_2(g) + H_2O(g)$

_____

_____

_____

_____

_____

Acid-Base Chemistry

Lesson #6 – Defining Acids and Bases

Objectives:

- To list both the physical and chemical properties of acids and bases

- To define acids and bases as they relate to the Arrhenius definition

- To define acids and bases as they relate to the Bronsted-Lowry definition

- To distinguish between strong and weak acids and bases, as well as list some common ones

- To describe the pH and POH scales

Introduction

What do tomato juice, drain and window cleaners, vinegar, vitamin C, mortar or plaster, and milk of magnesia all have in common? Other than being common household products, each of the products mentioned above is either an acid or a base. It is hard to imagine that things commonly found around us can actually teach us quite a bit about the nature of acid-base chemistry. This chapter will act as an introduction to acids and bases, and the chemical theories surrounding them.

Properties of Acids and Bases

Let's recall the definitions of physical and chemical properties of matter. Physical properties can be observed without a change in the substance, while chemical properties are only observable when the substance is undergoing a chemical change.

Physical Properties

The word acid was derived from the Latin word acere, meaning "sour" because acids generally have a sour taste when dissolved in water. Bases tend to be bitter-tasting. Unfortunately, this property is sometimes difficult to determine because most acids and bases are not suitable for tasting. However, we can taste vinegar and milk of magnesia. Based on taste, which one is an acid? (vinegar), which one is a base? (milk of magnesia). Bases have a special property that causes them to feel soapy or slick to touch, while acids tend to cause a burning sensation when they come into contact with skin. Another physical property of acids and bases is how they react with litmus paper. Litmus paper is an indicator, which means that it changes color when in the presence of certain chemicals. Bases turn red litmus paper blue, while acids turn blue litmus paper red. Both acids and bases also have the ability to conduct an electric current, making them part of a category of substances called electrolytes.

Litmus Paper Changes Color

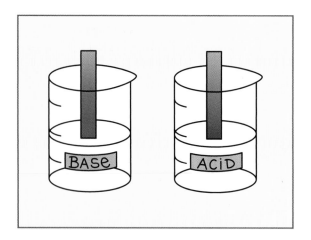

Chemical Properties

In a chemical reaction between an acid and a base, each one has the capability of destroying the chemical properties of the other. That is to say that a base destroys the chemical properties of an acid, and vice versa. This reaction is known as neutralization.

Another property of acids is that when they react with a reactive metal, such as an alkali metal or alkaline earth metal, they produce hydrogen gas.

$$\text{Mg (s)} + \text{H}_2\text{SO}_4 \text{ (aq)} \longrightarrow \text{H}_2 \text{ (g)} + \text{MgSO}_4 \text{ (aq)}$$

In order to continue with our definitions of acids and bases, we must be familiar with the scientific terms solution, solute and solvent, as well as recall the term ion. A solution is a homogeneous mixture of two or more pure substances. The solute is the substance that is dissolved by the solvent. When salt is dissolved in water, salt is the solute, while water is the solvent. Water is an excellent solvent for acids and bases, and a solution where water is the solvent is called an aqueous solution. In a chemical equation this is written as (aq).

Arrhenius Definition

Svante Arrhenius (1859-1927), a Swedish chemist and physicist, was one of the first scientific minds to define the terms acid and base, based not on observable properties, but rather on chemical structure.

Arrhenius Definition

Acids are molecular compounds containing hydrogen and when they are dissolved in water the bond between hydrogen and the rest of the molecule is broken. This process is known as ionization. The formation of freely moving ions under any circumstances is called ionization. The formation of freely moving ions, usually in a water solution, from ions that are bound together is called dissociation. Ions are electrically charged atoms (H^+) or group of atoms (OH^-).

$$HNO_3 \ (aq) \longrightarrow H^+ \ (aq) + NO_3^- \ (aq)$$

Often in an aqueous solution, the H^+ ion combines with a water molecule to form a hydronium ion (H_3O^+), but this is still designated as a hydrogen ion.

$$H^+ \ (aq) + H_2O \ (l) \longrightarrow H_3O^+ \ (aq)$$

Arrhenius defined a base as a substance that releases hydroxide ions (OH^-) when dissolved in water. Bases are ionic compounds composed of a positive and a hydroxide ion (negative ion). This process is known as dissociation – the process where ionic substances separate into ions when dissolved in a solvent.

$$NaOH \ (aq) \longrightarrow Na^+ \ (aq) + OH^- \ (aq)$$

This definition of acids and bases is limited because it only applies to situations where water is the solvent. In order to accommodate for other possibilities, scientists continued the search for a broader definition of acids and bases.

Bronsted-Lowry Definition

In 1923, within several months of one another, Johannes Bronsted from Denmark and Thomas Lowry of England separately published very similar theories about how acids and bases behave. Although somewhat inspired by Arrhenius, their theories were not limited to acids and bases as aqueous solutions.

They defined an acid as any substance that can donate H^+ to another substance. Remember that a hydrogen atom contains one electron and one proton, but a hydrogen ion is positive because it has lost its electron, therefore a hydrogen atom is simply a proton. Acids are proton donors. They defined a base as any substance that can remove H^+ from another substance. Bases are proton acceptors. It is important to understand that when the term "donate" is used, what is really meant is that a proton can be taken from acids, and bases are the substances doing the taking. Imagine a person walking down the street with money in their pocket, when all of a sudden they are pick-pocketed. This is how acids and bases behave. The acids have protons that the bases want, and so the bases take them. (See the pictorial on top of the next page.)

Some substances, such as water, can be both an acid and a base. Substances that have this ability to donate protons or accept protons are called amphoteric substances.

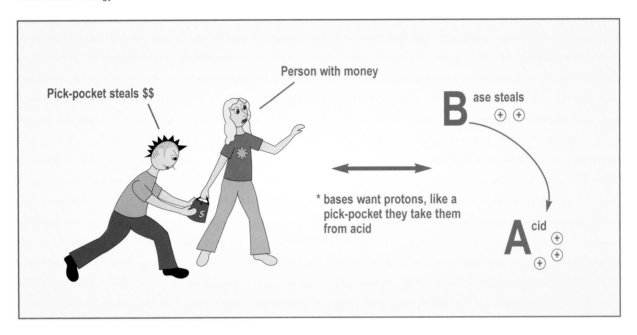

Strength of Acids and Bases

Let's review the analogy of the "pick-pocketer". Some bases are better than others in taking protons from acids. Imagine that you are about to be pick-pocketed, and you have two possible defenders; a big strong body builder or a decrepit older woman. Who would you choose? Probably the body builder because he would be able to hold onto your money better simply because he is stronger. Some bases are strong, meaning that they are able to take protons better than a weak base. Similarly, some acids are strong, meaning they are able to donate protons readily.

The strength of an acid is based on the concentration of hydrogen ions in solution. The strength of a base is determined by the concentration of hydroxide ions in solution.

A strong acid is one that is very good at transferring protons to solution, and therefore generates high concentrations of hydrogen ions in solution. In other words, a very strong acid will completely ionize in solution. This is indicated in the chemical equation by a single arrow from the reactants to products in the following example.

HCl
(hydrochloric acid):

$$HCl\ (g) + H_2O\ (l) \longrightarrow H_3O^+\ (aq) + Cl^-\ (aq)$$

A weak acid is one that does not transfer protons well to solution, and therefore produces lower concentrations of hydrogen ions in solution. A weak acid only partially ionizes in solution. This is shown in the chemical equation by a double arrow between the reactants and the products in the following example.

$HC_2H_3O_2$
(acetic acid):

$$HC_2H_3O_2 \text{ (aq)} + H_2O \text{ (l)} \rightleftharpoons H_3O^+ \text{ (aq)} + C_2H_3O_2^- \text{ (aq)}$$

A strong base is one that can easily remove protons from other substances, and generates high concentrations of hydroxide ions in solution. In other words, a very strong base will completely dissociate in solution.

NaOH
(sodium hydroxide):

$$NaOH \text{ (s)} \xrightarrow{H_2O} Na^+ \text{ (aq)} + OH^- \text{ (aq)}$$

A weak base does not remove protons from other substances easily, and therefore produces lower concentrations of hydroxide ions in solution. A weak base only partially dissociates in solution.

NH_3
(ammonia):

$$NH_3 \text{ (aq)} + H_2O \text{ (l)} \rightleftharpoons NH_4^+ \text{ (aq)} + OH^- \text{ (aq)}$$

The following table lists the most common acids and bases and their designations as either strong or weak.

Strength of Acids and Bases

STRONG ACIDS	STRONG BASES
H_2SO_4 (sulfuric acid)	Group IA (1) hydroxides
HCl (hydrochloric acid)	LiOH (lithium hydroxide)
HBr (hydrobromic acid)	NaOH (sodium hydroxide)
HI (hydriodic acid)	KOH (potassium hydroxide)
HNO_3 (nitric acid)	RbOH (rubidium hydroxide)
$HClO_4$ (perchloric acid)	CsOH (cesium hydroxide)
	Group IIA (2) hydroxides
	$Ca(OH)_2$ (calcium hydroxide)
	$Sr(OH)_2$ (strontium hydroxide)
	$Ba(OH)_2$ (barium hydroxide)

pH and pOH

As we have already discussed, the strength of an acid depends on how easily it will donate its protons, and the strength of a base depends on how easily it can remove protons from other substances. There is a means of expressing the strength of an acid or a base and it is called the pH scale.

pH is calculated by taking the negative logarithm of the concentration of hydrogen ions. Don't panic! It sounds more confusing than it is. A logarithm is simply the exponent part of a number expressed as a power of ten. For instance, the log of 2×10^4 is 4. The negative log would be -4. Calculating pH will best be explained by doing a sample calculation.

Gatorade has a hydrogen ion concentration of 8.0×10^{-4} mol/L. Calculate pH:

$$pH = -\log [H^+]$$
$$= -\log [8.0 \times 10^{-4}]$$
$$= -(-3.10)$$
$$= 3.10$$

Generally speaking, the range of H+ concentrations found in most acidic and basic solutions will range from: $1.0 \times 10^0 - 1.0 \times 10^{-14}$ moles per litre. Therefore, the range of the pH scale is 0-14.

• pH less than 7 means ACIDIC

• pH more than 7 means BASIC

• pH equal to 7 means NEUTRAL

A neutral pH simply means that the concentration of H^+ and OH^- is equal; therefore the solution is neither acidic nor basic.

The pOH scale is less commonly used, but is very similar to the pH scale in the way it is calculated. The only difference is that the pOH scale is based on the concentration of hydroxide ions (OH^-), not hydrogen ions. This means it is read opposite to the pH scale

• pOH less than 7 means BASIC

• pOH more than 7 means ACIDIC

• pOH equal to 7 means NEUTRAL

One interesting feature of the two scales is that when added together, they always equal a constant number, 14. So, if we know the pH of a substance, we can calculate its pOH and vice versa.

$$pH + pOH = 14.00$$

The following table shows the pH of some common substances.

	Solution	pH
Acidic	Lemon Juice	1.6 – 1.8
	Vinegar	2.5
	Soft Drinks	2.0 – 4.0
	Milk	6.3 – 6.6
	Saliva	6.2 – 7.4
Neutral	Pure Water	7.0
Basic	Blood	7.4
	Egg Whites	7.6 – 8.0
	Milk of Magnesia	10.5

Lesson Summary

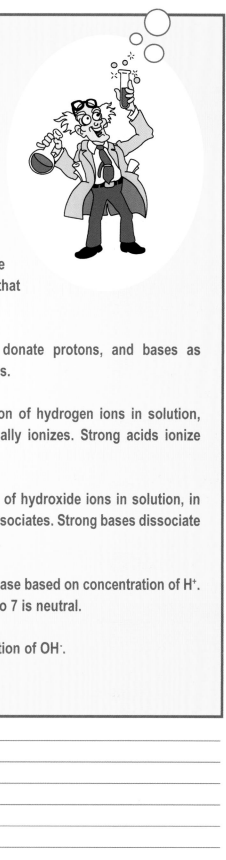

1. Acids taste sour, turn blue litmus paper red, conduct electricity, neutralize bases and produce hydrogen gas when reacted with a reactive metal.

2. Bases are bitter-tasting, feel soapy or slimy to touch, turn red litmus paper blue, conduct electricity, and neutralize acids.

3. Arrhenius defined acids as substances that release hydrogen ions in solution, and bases as substances that release hydroxide ions in solution.

4. Bronsted-Lowry defined acids as substances that donate protons, and bases as substances that remove protons from other substances.

5. The strength of an acid is based on the concentration of hydrogen ions in solution, in other words whether or not it completely or partially ionizes. Strong acids ionize completely, while weak acids only partially.

6. The strength of a base is based on the concentration of hydroxide ions in solution, in other words whether or not it completely or partially dissociates. Strong bases dissociate completely, while weak bases dissociate only partially.

7. pH is a scale that quantifies the strength of an acid or base based on concentration of H^+. Less than 7 is acidic, more than 7 is basic, and equal to 7 is neutral.

8. The pOH scale is opposite, and is based on concentration of OH^-.

Lesson #6 – Questions

1. Name 2 chemical and 2 physical properties of both an acid and a base.

_____

_____

_____

_____

_____

2. Define the terms ionization and dissociation. How do these processes lead to the formation of different strengths of acids?

_____

_____

_____

_____

_____

3. Compare the Arrhenius and the Bronsted-Lowry definitions of acids and bases.

_____

_____

_____

_____

_____

4. Classify each item listed below with a pH above, below, or equal to 7.

(a) lemon _____

(b) toilet cleaner _____

(c) vinegar _____

(d) water _____

(e) human blood _____

(f) baking soda _____

(g) sulphuric acid _____

Glossary

active transport – the movement of molecules against the regular grain of diffusion, costs the cell energy

adenosine triphosphate (ATP) – a molecule that stores energy until the cell requires it

alchemist – a scientific philosopher of the past

alkali metal – any of the highly reactive metals in Group 1 of the periodic table

alkaline earth metal – any of the reactive metals in Group 2 of the periodic table

allele – alternate forms of a gene

amino acid – the building blocks of protein

analogous structures – similar structures that have evolved independently of one another

angiosperm – a plant where the seed is enclosed in a fruit

anode – positively charged electrode

atom – the basic building block of matter

atomic mass – the mass of an average atom of a chemical element, measured in atomic mass units

atomic number – the number of protons in the nucleus of an atom

autotroph – an organism that produces its own food

capillary action – upwards movement of water due to the strong attraction of the water molecules to the sides of the xylem

cathode – negatively charged electrode

cell – smallest unit of life that can still perform all the life processes

Glossary

cell membrane – the outer boundary of the cell that controls the flow of materials in and out of the cell

cell nucleus – the organelle that directs all cell activities

cellular respiration – process whereby living organisms convert energy from food into a useable energy for the cell

cephalisation – the process of evolving head and tail ends

chemical property – these characteristics of substances can only be observed when a change in substance occurs; e.g. iron reacting with oxygen to form rust

chemical reaction (or change) – the irreversible process where the particles of matter have been changed permanently to form a new substance

chlorophyll – substance found in chloroplasts, used to capture the sun's energy for photosynthesis

chloroplasts – plant organelles needed for photosynthesis

chromosome – structure found in the nucleus of eukaryotic cells, made of DNA

cladistics – a branch of taxonomy that uses shared derived characteristics to determine the order of branching events from the common ancestor

cladogram – a diagram that shows evolutionary relationships between organisms

cloning – to make an identical copy of something

co-dominance – type of heredity where there is evidence of both traits being expressed in the same individual

codon – a sequence of three bases that codes for a particular amino acid

colloid – a type of mechanical mixture where the particles are so tiny that gravity does not cause them to settle at the bottom, so they remain suspended

compound – a pure substance made of two or more chemical elements in a fixed ratio

convergent evolution – two species have developed similar structures as a result of having similar habitats

cotyledon – plant structure that stores extra food and nutrients which are made available to the embryo upon germination

covalent bond (or molecular bond) – forms when one or more electrons are shared between atoms

crossing-over – the exchange of genetic material between homologous chromosomes during meiosis

cross-pollination – this process occurs when the pollen from one flower gets transferred to another

cuticle – waxy layer on the outside of most plants

cytokinesis – the final stage of mitosis, the division of the cytoplasm and all other organelles

density – a measure of how much "stuff" can fit into a particular space, is calculated by dividing an object's mass by its volume

deoxyribonucleic acid (DNA) – a molecule that contains the genetic information for protein synthesis in organisms

dicot – an angiosperm that has two cotyledons

diffusion – the movement of solute across a membrane from an area of high concentration to an area of low concentration

diploid – describes cells that have a paternal and maternal set of chromosomes

dissociation – the process where ionic substances separate into ions when dissolved in a solvent

dominant allele – expressed physically in individuals who possess it

ectoderm – the outer layer of cells in an animal, usually gives rise to skin

Glossary

electrolysis – the process of passing electricity through a substance in order to break it into smaller components

electron – tiny negatively charged particle found inside the atom, orbiting the nucleus

element – a pure substance made of only one type of atom that cannot be further broken down

embryo – a fertilized egg that has started to develop

endocytosis – moves molecules into the cell by engulfing them with arm-like extensions from the membrane

endoderm – the inner layer of cells in an animal, usually gives rise to the gut

energy – does not have mass and does not occupy space, cannot be created or destroyed, is capable of doing work

enzyme – a molecule that speeds up a reaction in the body

eukaryotic cell – has a membrane-bound nucleus and organelles

evolution – a genetic change in a species that has occurred over time

exocytosis – moves molecules out of the cell by fusing with the membrane

facilitated diffusion – the movement of molecules through protein channels, as opposed to the membrane

fertilization – the fusion of the sperm and the egg

gametes – sex cells; sperm in males and egg in females

gas discharge tube – a sealed tube holding gas at low pressures, electricity is passed through it

gastrulation – the formation of different layers of cells

gene – piece of a DNA molecule which codes for a specific trait

genotype – the combinations of the alleles

genus – a grouping for organisms that share major characteristics

germination – cracking of the seed for growth

gymnosperm – a plant that does not produce flowers or fruit

halogen – any of the highly reactive non-metals in Group 17 of the periodic table

haploid – describes cells that have only one set of chromosomes; example is sex cells

heterogeneous – term used to describe mixtures that do not have a uniform composition

heterotroph – an organism that is dependent on other organisms to obtain food

heterozygous – term used to describe individuals with two different forms of an allele for a particular trait

homeostasis – an organisms' ability to maintain a stable internal environment

homogeneous – term used to describe either pure substances or mechanical mixtures that have a uniform composition

homologous chromosomes – chromosomes that code for the same genes but are not identical, one is paternal and one is maternal

homozygous – term used to describe individuals with two of the same alleles for a particular trait

hydronium ion – H_3O^+

hydrophilic – water-attracting

hydrophobic – water-repelling

Glossary

hydroxide ion – OH⁻

incomplete dominance – type of heredity where neither allele is dominant, therefore the heterozygous individuals express a blend of the two possible phenotypes

ion – a charged atom, can be positive or negative

ionic bond – forms when positive and negative ions attract, electrons are donated

ionization – when a covalent compound dissolves to produce ions

isotope – any of two or more chemical elements with the same number of protons but different number of neutrons

karyotype – an entire set of chromosomes

kinetic energy – energy resulting from the movement of particles in matter

law of conservation of energy – states that energy can neither be created nor destroyed but may be transformed from one form to another

law of conservation of mass – states that mass can neither be created nor destroyed, and the total mass of the substances involved in a reaction remains constant

law of definite proportions – states that a compound is a pure substance formed when two or more atoms bond together in a fixed proportion

law of independent assortment – states that two or more pairs of alleles segregate independently of one another during meiosis

law of segregation – states that the members of each pair of alleles separate when gametes are formed

litmus paper – an indicator used to test pH of a substance

matter – the physical material that makes up the universe, it has mass and volume

mechanical mixture – made of one or more types of particles that do not have a fixed ratio

meiosis – a form of cell division that produces haploid cells (gamete production)

meristem – region in plants where cells undergo mitosis

mesoderm – the middle layer of cells in an animal, usually gives rise to organs

metabolism – an organisms' ability to use energy

metal – a chemical element that conducts electricity very well, has a metallic lustre, is ductile and malleable, such as aluminum or gold

metalloid – a chemical element that possesses properties of both metals and non-metals

mitosis – the process where the nucleus of a cell divides to form two identical daughter cells

molecular bond (or covalent bond) – forms when one or more electrons are shared between atoms

monocot – an angiosperm that has one cotyledon

multiple alleles – type of heredity where more than two alleles exist for the same trait

mycorrhizae – tiny structures on the roots of plants which allow them to absorb nutrients from the soil

natural selection – survival of the fittest

neutrons – particles with no charge found inside the nucleus of the atom

noble gas – any of the non-reactive non-metals in Group 18 of the periodic table

non-metal – a chemical element that does not possess the properties of metals

nucleotide – a unit of DNA consisting of a sugar, a phosphate and a base

Glossary

oogenesis — egg production (meiosis)

organelle — mini-organs that carry out specialized functions within the cell

osmosis — the movement of water across a membrane from an area of high concentration to an area of low concentration

particle theory of matter — a scientific model stating that all matter is made of tiny particles

periodic table — a table where the elements are arranged according to their properties and atomic masses

pH scale — a scale that expresses the strength of an acid or a base

phenetics — a branch of taxonomy that examines as many similar characteristics as possible to look for an overall degree of similarity between two organisms

phenotype — the physical traits that are expressed in the individual

phloem — tubing that carries the minerals, sugars and other nutrients to the entire plant

phospholipid — a molecule that has two parts: a head (water-attracting) and two tails (water-repelling)

photosynthesis — process used by plants to produce their own food

physical property — a characteristic of a substance that can be observed without a change in substance; examples are color, odor, density, boiling and melting points

physical reaction (or change) — a change in matter where no new substance is formed, reversible process

pistil — female part of the flower, consisting of stigma, style and ovary

plasmid — a ring of bacterial DNA that lies outside of the single chromosome in a bacterial cell

polar molecule — any molecule that has a positive and a negative end; example is water

pollination – the delivery of the sperm-containing pollen from its production site to location of the egg

potential energy – energy resulting from the position of an object in space, has the ability to do work

primary growth – occurs at root tips and increases plant length in both directions

prokaryotic cell – does not have a nucleus or organelles

proton – positively charged particle found inside the nucleus of the atom

punnett square – a tool used for predicting the outcomes of various crosses

pure substance – a substance made of only one type of particle

pure-breeding – term used to describe organisms that have only one type of allele for a particular gene

recessive allele – trait is not expressed in heterozygous individuals

restriction enzyme – an enzyme which recognizes a certain base sequence and cuts it at a particular point in that sequence

scientific method – an investigation that involves a specific set of steps involving experimentation, observation, measurement and analysis of collected data

secondary growth – causes an increase to the thickness of the plant

seed – a plant embryo

self-pollination – this process occurs when the pollen from a flower falls into the pistil of the same flower

sister chromatids – two identical chromosomes

solute – a substance that dissolves in a solvent

solution – a homogeneous mixture of two or more pure substances

Glossary

solvent – a substance that is able to dissolve a solute to form a solution

species – a group of organisms that are able to interbreed to produce fertile offspring

spermatogenesis – sperm production (meiosis)

spore – a single asexual reproduction cell that can develop into an organism

stamen – male part of the flower, consisting of anther and filament

stomata – tiny pores in the surface of leaves

suspension – the particles can be seen and will eventually settle to the bottom due to gravity

taxonomy – the science of classifying living organisms

tissue – a group of cells organized into a coordinated and functional unit

transcription – the process where a copy of DNA is made and the product is a single strand of ribonucleic acid (RNA)

translation – the process where the cell ribosomes decode the sequence of bases to make proteins

transpiration – the process whereby water is released from a plant

valence electrons – the electrons in the outermost shell of an atom

valency – the number of bonds an atom can form

vascular tissue – set of tubes that carry water and nutrients to every part of the plant

xylem – tubing that carries and distributes water to the entire plant

Answers to Questions

UNIT 1: ECOLOGY

Lesson #1

1. A population is a group of organisms of the same species living in one place, and a community is a group of interacting populations living in one place.

2. An ecosystem is a community of living things together with its environment. A field ecosystem would include all of the plants, animals and microorganisms living in that field along with the sun, air, water, nutrients, and soil.

3. The biotic factor can be any plant, animal or microrganism found in the ecosystem. The abiotic factor is any non-living thing in the ecosystem such as the sun, air, soil, wind.

4. Green plants are producers because they are able to produce their own food. Green plants capture the energy from the sun and use it to make sugars through the process of photosynthesis.

5. (a) consumer or heterotroph
   (b) omnivore
   (c) decomposer
   (d) herbivore

Lesson #2

1. (a) grass
   (b) prairie dog
   (c) golden eagle
   (d) grass
   (e) golden eagle

2. Detritus feeders and decomposers feed on and breakdown the dead organisms and waste at every trophic level. The detritus feeders and decomposers release nutrients into the ecosystem when they breakdown the waste and organisms.

3. Energy from the sun is captured by green plants through photosynthesis. The energy stored in the plants then moves through the food chain as one organism consumes the next.

4. Only 10% of the energy captured by an organism is transferred to the next trophic level. As we move up trophic levels, less and less energy is available to the organisms. By the time we reach the fourth trophic level, there is only a small percentage left of the original energy that entered the ecosystem. If there were more trophic levels, there may not be enough energy to support the organisms in the higher trophic levels.

Lesson #3

1. A nutrient cycle is the movement of chemical elements through ecosystems. In a nutrient cycle, the chemical element is found in the environment, moves into the food chain, and is then cycled back to the environment again. This process repeats itself over and over again.

2. Carbon, oxygen nitrogen, phosphorus, sulfur, zinc, sodium, copper, and iodine.

3. Since there is only a limited amount of nutrients in ecosystems, the nutrients would run out if they were not recycled. Without sufficient nutrients, the organisms in the ecosystem would die.

Lesson #4

1. Carbon is the building block for all organic molecules such as proteins, carbohydrates, and fats.

2. (a) False. Photosynthesis removes carbon dioxide from the atmosphere and adds oxygen to the atmosphere.

    (b) True

(c) False. When an animal dies decomposers consume the dead organism. They use the process of cellular respiration to obtain energy from the carbohydrates they ingest. As a result, carbon dioxide is released to the atmosphere, returning the carbon in the dead organisms to the carbon cycle.

3. Through the process of photosynthesis, plants remove carbon dioxide from the air and incorporate the carbon in their tissues. The carbon in the plant is now available to the organisms that consumes the plant. The carbon is now part of the food chain. The carbon moves through the food chain as one organisms consumes the next.

4. The carbon cycle is balanced by photosynthesis removing carbon dioxide from the environment and cellular respiration returning carbon dioxide to the environment. When there are fewer trees, there is less photosynthesis occurring. When there is less photosynthesis, it means that there is less carbon dioxide being removed from the atmosphere. Therefore, the level of carbon dioxide builds up in the atmosphere.

Lesson #5

1. (a) eutrophication
   (b) nitrogen fixation
   (c) Rhizobia
   (d) ammonia
   (e) denitrification

2. Nitrogen fixing bacteria convert the nitrogen gas in the atmosphere to a form that can be absorbed by the roots of plants. Without the nitrogen fixing bacteria, plants would not be able to absorb nitrogen and the nitrogen could not enter the food chain.

3. When decomposers break down dead organisms, ammonia is released into the soil. Nitrifying bacteria convert the ammonia into nitrates. Denitrifying bacteria convert the nitrates back into nitrogen gas that is released into the atmosphere.

Lesson #6

1. (a) The source of carbon and nitrogen for ecosystems is the atmosphere, whereas the source of phosphorus is rock.

    (b) Phosphorus takes much longer to cycle through an ecosystem than nitrogen and carbon. It takes a long time to remove phosphorus from rock through the weathering process.

2. (a) fertilizers, animal wastes from livestock, municipal sewage

    (b) eutrophication of lakes

3. Insert diagram: Correct order is nutrient in rock or atmosphere, nutrient absorbed by plant, nutrient moves through food chain, decomposers break down dead organisms, nutrient released to environment.

4. The water can fall as precipitation directly back into the ocean. The water can fall as precipitation on land and then move along the surface of the land back into the ocean. The water can fall as precipitation on land, get absorbed by the ground, enter the groundwater, and eventually drain into the ocean through cracks and pores in rocks.

5. Any three of using water for irrigating crops, water use in industry and homes, building dams, desalination, using groundwater.

Lesson #7

1. Climate is the average weather conditions of an area over many years. Temperature and rainfall are the two most important elements of climate.

2. Pieces of weathered rock, decaying plant and animal matter, a variety of microrganisms, water.

3. Soil characteristics influence which plants and therefore which animals can survive in an ecosystem. Different plants are better suited to the different textures, depths, and nutrient contents of the soils.

4. Microrganisms move around in the soil creating air spaces. Some microrganisms decompose dead plant and animal matter, adding nutrients to the soil.

Lesson #8

1. (a) False. Organisms are adapted to their environments. If they change the environment in which they live, they may not have the necessary tools and strategies to cope with the new environmental conditions.

   (b) False. Only a small variety of plants and animals can cope with extreme conditions.

   (c) True

   (d) True

2. The sandpiper lives on sandy shores of oceans and eats insects. Its long thin beak allows it to pick insects out of the sand.

3. Activities that affect biodiversity are clear-cutting forests, draining wetlands, selling exotic pets, pollution, hunting, and over-fishing.

Lesson #9

1. Primary succession is the formation of an ecosystem from scratch, on bare rock. Secondary succession is the formation of a new ecosystem after an already existing ecosystem has been disturbed.

2. (f), (d), (c), (a), (g), (b), (e)

3. Secondary succession occurs after a forest fire, forming a new forest ecosystem on the burned ground. Secondary succession occurs when there has been a nutrient influx into lakes, resulting in a meadow.

4. (a) pioneer organisms
   (b) biome
   (c) tropical rainforest
   (d) climax community

5. (a) desert
   (b) grasslands
   (c) tundra
   (d) chaparral

Lesson #10

1. Humans depend on nature for a variety of goods and services such as food, shelter, energy sources such as oil, waste absorption, and protection from the sun's ultraviolet rays afforded by the ozone layer.

2. An ecological footprint measures the amount of land and water that is needed to support the way of life of a person or a population. The ecological footprint is calculated by adding the amount of land you occupy to the amount of land needed to produce your resources and absorb your wastes.

Lesson #11

1. All organisms in an ecosystem are interconnected. DDT residue on plants spread to other organisms through the food web, spreading the effect of the DDT to a large area. The chemical accumulated in the fat in animals higher up on the food chain.

2. Sustainable living is using nature's goods and services in such a way that resources are not degraded or depleted for future generations.

3. The effects of clear-cutting depletes forest resources for future generations. Clear-cutting reduces biodiversity, causes soil erosion, and removes nutrients from the soil.

4. If the deer were protected, their growing population would have several negative effects on the natural ecosystem and humans. The large deer population would damage forest vegetation, spread deer ticks that carry Lyme disease, and damage agricultural land. Controlling the deer population would sustain the forests and benefit the human population.

UNIT 2: BIOLOGY

Lesson #1

1. Multi-cellular organisms have an advantage over unicellular organisms because their cells can specialize for certain functions. This specialization means that each cell has to do less, and they can become very good at what they do.

2. There are two types of surface proteins that allow cells to communicate with one another. Receptor proteins are able to receive chemical and electrical messages sent by other cells. Marker proteins are like name tags for each cell, and they tell other cells information about their functions in the body.

3. The cells has many different ways of transporting materials in and out of the cell; diffusion, osmosis, facilitated diffusion, and active transport.

   (a) Diffusion is the movement of solids across a membrane, while osmosis is the movement of water across a membrane. In both cases, movement of the substance occurs from an area of high concentration to an area of low concentration. This does not require energy.

   (b) Facilitated diffusion is very similar to diffusion, but the molecule does not pass directly through the membrane. Instead, the molecule slides through a protein channel. This does not require energy.

(c) In active transport, the protein channels move molecules against the regular grain of diffusion. This process requires energy.

(d) Endocytosis moves large molecules into the cell by engulfing them with arm-like extensions from the membrane. Exocytosis moves large molecules out of the cell by fusing with the membrane. Both processes require energy.

4. Photosynthesis and cellular respiration are the exact opposite processes Photosynthesis produces oxygen and sugar, while cell respiration requires oxygen and sugar.

Lesson #2

1. Muscle cells carry the diploid number of chromosomes while sperm cells carry the haploid number. In humans this means that muscle cells contains 46 chromosomes (23 from each parent), while the sperm cell only contains 23.

2. Cytokinesis is the final stage of mitosis where the two daughter cells physically split from one another. In animals, the cell membrane pinches from the outside in. In plants, a cell plate grows from the inside out and eventually builds a wall between the two cells.

3. The cell cycle consists of 2 major phases – interphase and mitosis. Interphase consists of more than 90% of the cell's time, and is devoted primarily to growth and replication of chromosomes. Mitosis takes up only a small amount of the cell's cycle, but it is very important because it is what allows the cells to divide.

4. Mitosis is the division of cells to produce two identical daughter cells. This process allows the cell to grow.

5. Mitosis and meiosis are very similar processes; however their results are very different. Mitosis produces two identical daughter cells, whereas meiosis produces four non-identical cells that contain only half the chromosomes as the original cell.

6. Crossing over is the exchange of genetic material between homologous chromosomes in the early stages of meiosis. This ensures variety within species because it means that each of the 4 haploid cells produced will not be identical. Each offspring born through sexual reproduction will be genetically different (except for identical twins).

Lesson #3

1. Let T = tongue rolling, Let t = non-tongue rolling

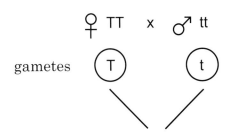

♀ TT   x   ♂ tt

gametes   (T)   (t)

Tt   ∴ all offspring will be heterozygous, therefore 100% will be tongue-rollers

2.   TTYY   x   TtYy

gametes   (TY)   (TY) (Ty) (tY) (ty)

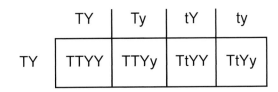

	TY	Ty	tY	ty
TY	TTYY	TTYy	TtYY	TtYy

∴ all plants will be tall with yellow seeds

3.   white   x   roan

          WW   x   RW

gametes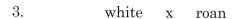

	R	W
W	RW	WW

∴ 50% will be white, and 50% will be roan

4. Incomplete dominance

    If all the F1 are pink, they have genotype rw

    the only 2 alleles are (r) and (w)

    ∴ parents must be rr and ww

5.   1^A 1^B (x 1^B 1^B
              or 1^B 1^B)

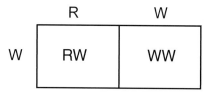

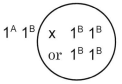

gametes

⇨

or
	1^B	1^B	1^O
1^A	1^A 1^B	1^A 1^B	1^A 1^O
1^B	1^B 1^B	1^B 1^B	1^B 1^O

Lesson #4

1. DNA is a double-helix structure, meaning it looks much like a ladder. The legs of the ladder are made of sugar and phosphate; while the rungs of the ladder are made of bases. It is a large chain of nucleotides, where each nucleotide consists of one sugar, one phosphate and one base.

2. Translation is the process where the cell ribosomes decode the sequence of bases to make proteins. Therefore, the purpose of translation is to take the genetic information held by the DNA and use it to create and build proteins.

3. Restriction enzymes are used to separate or isolate one gene from all of the other genes. They work by cutting DNA at very specific points in their base sequences, much like a pair of scissors might. Each restriction enzyme has a certain sequence, called a recognition sequence, which it cuts when found.

4. Plasmids are rings of bacterial DNA that lie outside of the single chromosome in a bacterial cell. They make excellent vehicles for DNA because they are able to move freely in and out of bacterial cells, incorporating the new gene into the DNA production of the cell.

5. Here is an overview of the basic steps that were taken to clone the very first organism, Dolly the sheep:

   - The DNA of a sheep was donated in the form of a few udder cells.
   - An egg cell of a second sheep was also donated, and the nucleus containing the DNA of this egg was removed.
   - The DNA from the first donor was fused with the empty egg from the second donor, using a powerful jolt of electricity.
   - The DNA in the egg is reprogrammed, by the organelles of the egg cell, to act like an embryo.
   - This egg cell is implanted in the uterus of a third sheep, a surrogate mother.
   - The resulting offspring is an exact clone of the sheep that donated the DNA.

Lesson #5

1. Using an organism's common name can be confusing because there may be more than one common name, but also because common names are used in many different languages. The naming system we have eliminates confusion among languages because it is all done in Latin.

2. Convergent evolution means that two species have developed similar structures, likely as a result of having similar habitats. These are called analogous structures because they evolved independently, not from a common ancestor. This can mislead scientists into thinking that animals share a common ancestor when they don't.

3. Kingdom, Phylum, Class, Order, Family, Genus, and Species

4. Cladistics uses shared derived characteristics to determine the order of branching events from the common ancestor. It is concerned only with evolutionary relationships, not classification. These relationships are represented in a diagram that resembles a tree, called a cladogram.

   Phenetics considers as many similar characteristics as possible to look for an overall degree of similarity between two organisms. Phenetics does not observe evolutionary relationships; it simply groups organisms so that naming can take place more easily.

Lesson #6

1. Marine plants had to overcome the obstacles presented by a dry environment by making adaptations to their structures. They developed an outer, waxy surface to reduce water loss, they developed seeds and spores in order to facilitate reproduction, and they developed mycorrhizae to help absorb nutrients from soil.

2. There are three methods which allow water to move against the force of gravity: osmosis, capillary action and cohesion of water molecules. Osmosis is the movement of water and it occurs from the soil into the plant, at the roots. From there capillary action takes over. This moves the water upwards due to the strong attraction of the water molecules to the sides of the xylem tubing. The final method of moving water

upwards in a plant occurs due to the cohesion of water molecules. Water molecules are powerfully attracted to one another, and so when water is being evaporated from the leaves (transpiration), the water molecules 'stick' to one another and hence move up towards the leaves.

3. Gymnosperms are wind-pollinated. This means that each of the pollen grains from the pollen cones are carried by the wind to the site of the fallen seed cones. Angiosperms can be wind-pollinated as well, but in most cases, however, it is insects and animals that complete pollination of angiosperms. Pollination of angiosperms is less limited, therefore more successful.

4. This occurs when the pollen from the anther simply falls onto the stigma and makes its way down the style to the ovary. In this case, the resulting plants will be identical copies of the original. Cross-pollination occurs when the pollen from one flower gets transferred to another and this ensures genetic recombination or variety among plants.

5. Those plants that produce seeds are able to thrive in much dryer and harsher conditions than those without because the protective covering around the seed prevents damage due to physical injury or drought. Also seeds are easily dispersed by insects and animals.

Lesson #7

1. Radial symmetry occurs when a cross-section can be taken so that both halves will be identical. Bilateral symmetry exists when you can make a cut from top to bottom along the front of an organism to produce identical pieces. Animals exhibiting bilateral symmetry have been evolutionarily more successful.

    There are three types of body cavities: acoelomate, pseudocoelomate, and coelomate. Acoelomates are organisms that do not have a body cavity. Pseudocoelomates have a cavity between the mesoderm and the endoderm. Coelomates have a true body cavity located within the mesoderm and this provides the most advantages to the organism. The major advantage is that the coelom allows the gut to function independently of the body wall and therefore can be much longer that the organism, which is better for absorption of nutrients.

2. The ectoderm always gives rise to the skin and/or the nervous tissue. The endoderm usually gives rise to tissue that forms the lining of the gut. The mesoderm tissue layer most often gives rise to muscle, reproductive,and circulatory organs.

3. Marine animals had to make several adaptations to be successful land-dwellers. They had to develop a means of physical support, waterproof skin, hearing mechanisms for air, a means of extracting oxygen from air, and a means of reproducing on land.

4. Answers may vary – see chart of characteristics. (lesson 7)

UNIT 3: CHEMISTRY

Lesson #1

1. Matter is the Physical Material of the world, it has mass and volume. Energy has neither mass nor volume, it gives matter the ability to do work.

2.

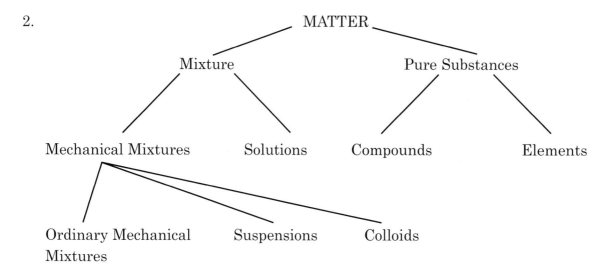

3. A piece of glass being smashed into tiny shards is an example of a physical change. There is no new substance formed, the size of the pieces of glass simply becomes much smaller. Also, there is no temperature or color change, there is no gas produced, and all of the initial substance is still present.

Rust formation on the underside of a car is an example of a chemical change. The presence of the new substance (rust) is the main indicator that a chemical change has taken place. This reaction is irreversible, and there is most definitely a color change.

4. Density = M/V
            = 50 g/10ml
            = 5 g/ml

Lesson #2

1. The scientific method is an investigation that involves a logical sequence of steps, such as forming a hypothesis, testing it through observation and measurement, analyzing the resulting data, and forming a conclusion.

2. Dalton's Theory basically said that all matter was made of tiny particles called atoms. He reasoned that there were different types of atoms and that when combined in different ways, new substances could be formed.

3. **Dalton's Model**

   – *"bowling ball"* model
   – indivisible sphere

Thomson's Model

   – *"blueberry muffin"* model
   – positive core
   – negative chunks throughout core

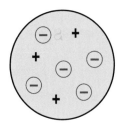

Rutherford's Model

– *"electron cloud"* model
– positive core called nucleus
– negative bits surround nucleus

Bohr-Rutherford Model

– *"modern-day"* model
– nucleus contains protons and neutrons
– electrons orbit nucleus

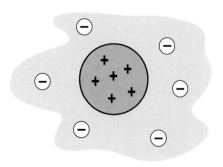
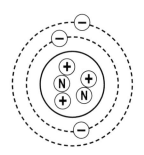

4. Rutherford performed an experiment using radioactive alpha (positively charged) particles and gold foil. He sent the beam of alpha particles through a very thin piece of gold foil. Some particles travelled straight through, however some of the particles also rebounded almost directly back off the foil. Rutherford reasoned that there must therefore be a dense positive portion of the atom that would cause this strong repelling reaction. Also, because most of the alpha particles did travel straight through, that there must be mostly empty space in an atom. This disproved Thompson's "blueberry muffin" model.

Lesson #3

1. It was important to develop an international naming system for the elements so that scientists all over the world could collaborate and share data.

2. Then Mendeleev began arranging the elements into a table based on their characteristics, there were some "holes" in the table. He suspected that these "holes" were elements that had not yet been discovered. He used these "holes" to predict characteristics of elements that hadn't been discovered, thereby narrowing the search.

Group #	Group Name	Group Characteristics
1	Alkali Metals	• Highly reactive • One electron in outer shell • React with exposure to air
2	Alkaline Earth	• Very reactive • Two electrons in outer shell
17	Halogens	• Highly reactive • Missing one electron in outer shell • Non-metals
18	Noble Gases	• Not reactive (inert) • Have full outer shells • Non-metals, gases

(preceded by) 3.

4. (a) Al – 13 protons, 13 electrons, 14 neutrons

(b) Ti – 22 protons, 22 electrons, 26 neutrons

(c) F – 9 protons, 9 electrons, 10 neutrons

(d) Xe – 54 protons, 54 electrons, 77 neutrons

Lesson #4

1. A valence electron is any electron found in the outermost shell (orbital) of an atom. An atom is most stable when its outer shell is full of electrons, and atoms always react in a way that allows them to stable. If an atom only has one electron, then it is highly reactive because it wants to get rid of that electron. If an atom is only missing one electron, then it is also highly reactive because it wants to gain an electron. The closer an atom is to achieving a full orbital, the more reactive it will be.

2.	Types of Bonding	
	Ionic	Molecular
	• electrons are exchanged between atoms • the bond is formed by the attraction of the newly formed ions • examples: KCI, HBr, NACl, HF	• electrons are shared between atoms • the atoms bonded together are neutrally charged • examples: H_2O, CH_4, H_2O_2, $C_6H_{12}O_6$

3. (a) 18   (b) 6   (c) 7   (d) 48

4. The law of definite proportions states that a compound is a pure substance formed when two or more atoms bond together in a fixed proportion. This means that compounds with different molecular formulas but with the same elements will have the same properties. (eg. Water H_2O and hydrogen peroxide H_2O_2)

Lesson #5

1. The law of conservation of energy states that energy can neither be created nor destroyed. The law of conservation of mass states that mass can neither be created nor destroyed.

2. (a) Combination or Synthesis reactions

    • The general formula for this is: A + Z – AZ

    (b) Decomposition reactions

    • The general formula for this is: AZ – A + Z

(c) Single Replacement reactions

- The general formula for this is: $A + BZ - B + AZ$

(d) Double Displacement reactions

- The general formula for this is: $AX + BZ - AZ + BZ$

3. (a) $Fe(s) + 2HCI(aq) \quad ----> \quad FeCl_2(aq) + H_2(g)$

   (b) $2C_4H_{10}(g) + 13O_2(g) \quad ----> \quad 8CO_2(g) + 10H_2O(g)$

Lesson #6

1.

	Acids	Bases
Physical Properties	• sour tasting • conduct electricity	• slippery feeling • conduct electricity
Chemical Properties	• can neutralize a base • release hydrogen gas when reacting with a metal	• can neutralize an acid

2. Ionization occurs when acids are part of an aqueous solution. It is the breaking of molecular bonds to produce ions. For example, when HCI (hydrochloric acid) is mixed with water, H^+ and Cl^- ions are released.

   Dissociation occurs when bases are part of an aqueous solution. It is the breaking of ionic bonds when acted on by a solvent (water). For example when NaOH (sodium hydroxide) is added to water, it dissociates to form ions Na^+ and OH^-.

3. Arrhenius defined acids as substances that produce hydrogen ions (H^+) in solution, and bases produced hydroxide ions (OH^-) in solution. Note that this definition only applies when water is the solution.

   Bronsted-Lowry revised Arrhenius' definition to include the possibility that water was not the solvent. Their definition says that acids donate protons (H^+), while bases remove protons.

4. (a) below
   (b) above
   (c) below
   (d) equal to
   (e) slightly above (almost neutral)
   (f) above
   (g) below